Roads, Bridges, and Tunnels

Other Books in this Series

Roads, Bridges, and Tunnels

Modern Approaches to Road Engineering

Michael Overman

Doubleday Science Series
Doubleday & Company, Inc.,
Garden City, New York, 1968

First published in the United States of America in 1968 by
Doubleday & Company, Inc., Garden City, New York,
in association with Aldus Books Limited.
Library of Congress Catalog Card No. 68-18088
Copyright © Aldus Books Limited, London, 1968
Printed in Italy by Arnoldo Mondadori, Verona

Contents

Picture Credits

Page 8 Autostrade Company, Roma: 15 *Illustrated London News:* 19 Photo British Travel Association: 25 Anglian Building Products Limited, Norwich, Norfolk: 28 Photo F. S. Lincoln from Paul Popper Ltd.: 31 Photo Ruston-Bucyrus Ltd., Lincoln, England: 36 Photo Lockwood Survey Corporation: 51 From *Engineering News-Record*, August 13 1964 © Mc Graw-Hill Inc: 53, 54 Photos Ishikawajima-Harima Heavy Industries Co., Ltd.: 55 *Engineering*, London: 58 From Rolt Hammond, A.C.G.I., A.M.I.C.E., *Modern Civil Engineering Practice*, Newnes, 1961: 60 Compactors Engineering Ltd.: 65 James T. Jenkins, Jr., Editor *American Road Builder Magazine:* 68 Amey's Asphalt Co., Ltd., Sutton Courtenay, Berks, England: 71 Cement and Concrete Association, London: 72 *Engineering,* London: 73 Photo courtesy City Engineer & Surveyor, Manchester County Borough, and G. Maunsell & Partners, Consulting & Chartered Engineers: 76 Fox Photos Ltd.: 81 (Top & bottom) 83 Courtesy Rowland J. Mainstone, from H. Shirley-Smith, *The World's Great Bridges*, Phoenix House, 1964: 84 Photo INBEL: 85 Courtesy Rowland J. Mainstone, *The World's Great Bridges*: 87 Photo U.S. Army Corps of Engineers, Washington, D.C. 20315, U.S.A.: 90 Alcan Aluminium Limited: 94 Rolt Hammond, A.C.G.I., A.M.I.C.E., *Civil Engineering Today* O.U.P. 1960: 96 (Bottom left) From H. E. Dance, *Engineers at Work*: 98, 99 Council of the Institution of Civil Engineers, London: 100 Rolt Hammond, *Modern Civil Engineering Practice*: 101 (Left) Courtesy Rowland J. Mainstone, from *The World's Great Bridges*: 101 (Right) William Tribe Ltd.: 104 Triborough Bridge and Tunnel Authority, New York: 108 Photo courtesy The Port of New York Authority: 109 (Top) Cement and Concrete Association: 109 (Bottom) Department of Roads, New South Wales: 110 New Haven Railroad: 111 Courtesy Rowland J. Mainstone, from *The World's Great Bridges*: 112 (Top and center) Rolt Hammond, *Civil Engineering Today:* 112 (Bottom) From H. E. Dance, *Engineers at Work*: 117 Courtesy Rowland J. Mainstone, from *The World's Great Bridges*: 123 Rolt Hammond *Civil Engineering Today* and Courtesy the Council of the Institution of Civil Engineers, London: 126 From H. E. Dance, *Engineers at Work*: 128 Photo Reed and Mallik Ltd.: 129 (Bottom) Photo by permission of the Venezuelan Embassy, London: 132 (Top right) Courtesy Rowland J. Mainstone, from *The World's Great Bridges*: 132, 133 Triborough Bridge and Tunnel Authority, New York: 136 Atlas Copco: 140 Rolt Hammond, *Modern Civil Engineering Pactice*: 143 From *Engineering News-Record* August 13 1964 © McGraw-Hill Inc.: 144 *Illustrated London News:* 147 Rolt Hammond *Modern Civil Engineering Practice*: 148, 149 Sir Robert McAlpine & Sons Ltd. (Equipment Sales Division): 150, 153 (Top) Rolt Hammond *Modern Civil Engineering Practice*: 153 (Bottom) Photo Christiani and Neilson Ltd.: 154 *Engineering*, London: 156 Chesapeke Bay Bridge and Tunnel District: 159 Courtesy London Transport Board: 162, 163 From H. E. Dance, *Engineers at Work*: 164, 165 *Engineering,* London: 167 From *Engineering News-Record*, August, 13, 1964, © Mc Graw-Hill, Inc.: 169 Rolt Hammond, *Civil Engineering Today* and Courtesy the Council of the Institution of Civil Engineers, London: 170 Sir William Halcrow and Partners: 174 *Design and Components*: 177 Bureau of Public Roads, U.S. Department of Commerce, Washington, D.C.: 183 Whittaker, Hunt & Co. Ltd.: 184 From L. K. Edwards, *High Speed Tube Transportation*, © *Scientific American*, Inc. 1965 All rights reserved: 186 French Embassy, London.

1   What is Civil Engineering?

An American wit once described a civil engineer as a man who can "do for one dollar what any darn fool can do for two." He oversimplified, no doubt; but his humor only disguises the truth. For in this electronic age, when microminiaturization packs an entire circuit into a plastic pinhead, the civil engineer, by contrast, reckons the rock he has to cut and cart in tens of thousands of costly metric tons. While the physicist measures the wavelength of a laser beam in angstroms because the micron is an inconveniently large unit, the civil engineer calculates the high-tensile steel wire requirement for the cables of a modern suspension bridge in thousands of costly kilometers. And while the adventurous heart surgeon today might implant a button-sized electrical cell to aid an ailing human heart with a 10-year power boost, the civil engineer might consider an underground nuclear explosion as a means to help him do for one million dollars what tradition, using dynamite, can only do for two million.

Civil engineering is shaking the earth. It is tunneling under

Bridges and tunnels on Italy's 755-km. Autostrada del Sole from Milan to Naples. Completed in 1964, this remarkable civil engineering achievement incorporates 113 large bridges, 20 km. of tunnels, and some 570 flyovers. It was built for a nonprofit-making organization and is paid for by means of a system of tolls.

mountains; it is bridging wide waterways and gorges. It is opening up thousands of kilometers of transport routes—transcontinental freeways, rapid transit railroads, canals, and seaways. It is building airports from which massive supersonic airliners can fly; it is creating great harbors secure from the open sea. Civil engineering is damming rivers, taming millions of kilograms of swirling waters. It is raising heart-warming buildings that reach up to the sky; it is lining the reactor chambers of nuclear power stations with walls impervious forever to the most concentrated radioactivity. It is balancing 2-million-kg. radio-telescope dishes so that they can accurately focus the weakest of electromagnetic signals from outer space; it is spanning vast spaces with self-supporting geodesic domes. Civil engineering is building foundations that will stand the ever-increasing loads that engineers choose to place upon them. And, since intellectual man strives for something finer than mere physical achievement, the civil engineer of distinction is at heart an architect as well.

Civil engineering is as old as history. Strabo has recorded that Babylon had paved roads over 4000 years ago; Herodotus wrote of a great Babylonian bridge across the Euphrates, wooden beams on stone piers, in 2230 B.C.; and another historian tells of a foot tunnel under the same great river in 2160 B.C. Nor is civil engineering's leviathan scale a product only of contemporary technology. The Pharaoh Khufu, better known as Cheops, raised the Great Pyramid at Giza in about 2700 B.C. This masterpiece of primitive civil engineering was built 144 m. high, stands on a perfect 227-m. square (the maximum length measurement error was less than 0.1 per cent, of the right angles less than 1/300 of a degree), and was built of several million tons of massive granite blocks, cut from solid rock with carborundum-tipped saws, say the experts; the Pharaoh's engineers were evidently not lacking in technology. But if the contemporary engineer has exciting new materials with which to design, he cannot afford to employ some 300,000 men for 20 years to build a pyramid, as Pharaoh Khufu did. How does he solve the problems of the 1960s? How does he fight his battle with the virus of rising costs? How does he succeed in doing for one dollar what any darn fool can do for two? That is what this book is about.

The tapestry of civil engineering is almost endless. And though it has common threads running through it, the same colors occurring again and again, the picture is far too complex to describe in a single slim volume. We must therefore be selective. Civil engineering works fall into three distinct areas—transport, irrigation and power, and general construction. The main ingredient of construction work is building in all its diversity. It includes such sophisticated new techniques as industrialized housing using factory-made components, the erection of custom-built lighthouses from prefabricated parts, the design and erection of huge scientific instruments like the 75-m. Jodrell Bank radio telescope, and the construction of launching towers and pads for ever bigger space rockets.

In the sphere of power and irrigation are some of the greatest of all engineering projects—gigantic dams forming vast artificial lakes and the canals and water tunnels often associated with them, hydroelectric and nuclear power stations and their distribution networks, and great schemes for generating power from the rise and fall of the tide. But most diverse of all is the field of transport, covering airfields, railroads, and roads, the bridges and tunnels that highways and railroads require, and water transportation facilities such as canals, seaways, and harbors. It is transportation engineering to which this book will confine itself; and even here the area is so great that the reader must satisfy himself for the present with the civil engineering of land transport and airfields, leaving waterways for another occasion.

How then are roads and airfields built? How are railroads laid down? What are the engineering secrets of bridge building and tunneling? First let us explore, very briefly, the ground that is common to all civil engineering. The main elements are three: materials, power, and ingenuity.

The Great Pyramid was built of an estimated 2,300,000 granite blocks. The Ancient Israelites made and used bricks, as we know from the Old Testament. For lesser work, timber has always been widely used. But today steel and concrete have elbowed out the masonry and bricks that held the field for thousands of years, and wood has been joined by plastics; machines have made the muscles that raised pyramids as high as 40-storey houses seem

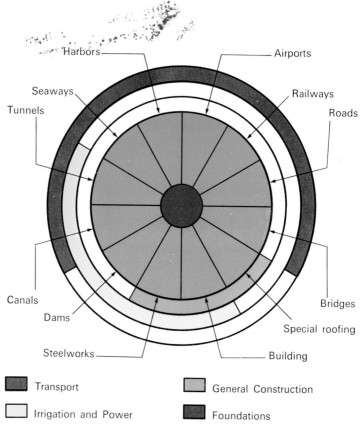

Harbors — Airports
Seaways — Railways
Tunnels — Roads
Canals — Bridges
Dams — Special roofing
Steelworks — Building

■ Transport   ■ General Construction
□ Irrigation and Power   ■ Foundations

Road, bridge, and tunnel construction seen in the general context of civil engineering. Transportation in all its forms provides the civil engineer with the greatest diversity of problems, while problems of foundations are common to all civil engineering projects.

puny; and ingenuity now has the advantage of a vast store of recorded experience on which to draw—of research, new technologies, and testing facilities unheard of even 50 years ago.

In modern practice, civil engineers have crystallized into two distinct groups—those who design (consultant engineers), and those who build (contractor's engineers). It is logical, therefore, to divide the technology of civil engineering into similar compartments—design and construction. But before we get to grips with the technicalities of design it will be helpful to take a quick look at the economic aspect of civil engineering, for this is a factor that exerts a far greater influence on the finished product than it does in other branches of advanced engineering.

The Economics of Civil Engineering

The reasons for this exceptional influence of money are not hard to find. Consider, first, a national space program. This is financed by a procedure that would go instantly to the head of any civil engineer. Decisions are taken, plans are drawn up, specifications are issued, contracts are awarded, and the nation is taxed to pay the bill. Provided the contractors' and suppliers' profits are fair and the wages correct, the actual cost of the project is of relatively minor consequence. In commercial engineering for mass production, whatever the political ideology of the state, the cost of research and development is almost invariably spread over a large number of the end product, and is thus easily absorbed.

But in civil engineering the cost of a single undertaking such as a bridge must be considered in isolation. True, some costly basic research may be used by the designers of future bridges, but the production order for any particular job is one. The prototype is the finished article; and because it has to be paid for as a single finished item, the engineer's problem is to finish his job at the minimum cost possible. When the decision was taken to throw a four-lane highway over the Firth of Forth, Scotland, near the old Forth railroad bridge, the problem was to design and build not necessarily a bridge, but the most economical crossing that would carry a stipulated volume of motor traffic of a specified maximum weight, leaving a defined minimum headroom over the water for shipping. In the event, three alternative schemes were investigated: a roadway under the rail track on the existing railroad bridge; a tunnel under the water; a new bridge, of whatever design. The first proposal ran into difficulties because a new steel substructure would have overloaded the existing bridge, and if made of aluminum there was a risk of corrosive electric currents at the interfaces between the two metals. A prefabricated immersed-tube tunnel seemed an attractive proposal. It would cause no navigation hazard at all and cost no more to build and less to maintain than a suitable bridge. But a long road tunnel must have efficient ventilation to remove the poisonous carbon monoxide constituent of automobile exhaust. The running cost of such ventilation plant turned the economic scales in favor of a new bridge. And the cheapest form of bridge to fulfil the stated requirements was a suspension bridge. So it was money that made the choice.

The world's greatest bridge today, the Verrazano-Narrows suspension bridge across the mouth of New York harbor, cost $325 million and was sponsored by a city authority. How could such a body finance such a project? By an issue of bonds. How are the bonds being redeemed? By collecting from every vehicle crossing the bridge a toll calculated not only to repay the borrowed money in a reasonable period, but also to meet interest charges and the cost of maintaining the bridge. The project, therefore, is financially self-supporting; and since the estimates of traffic were based on unimpeachable research, the bonds were virtually gilt-edged.

This system of financing expensive transportation works is growing steadily more popular with the authorities involved. Bridges, tunnels, and sometimes freeways are increasingly being paid for directly by the automobiles and trucks that use them daily. Sometimes this costs the motorist or motor transport operator precisely nothing, for the simple reason that the new bridge or tunnel or freeway reduces mileage and so saves gas and time worth more than the price of using it.

Aids to Engineering Design

There are four main aids to engineering design: survey, experience, research, and mathematics. Every civil engineering undertaking starts with a survey. The site is examined. The bearing strength of the ground is measured. If a tunnel is to be built the engineer must first find out how hard the rock is, or how wet the clay through which he is to dig. For a highway or railroad it may be a long-distance survey of a hilly tract that is needed to discover the most economical route.

The surveyor's level, the theodolite, the staff and the chain are in constant use. But today outline surveys are sometimes wanted of vast or almost inpenetrable regions; the quick method, in such cases, is stereophotography from aircraft, using especially designed instruments.

Drilling is commonly used to determine the depth of bedrock for major foundations, but new geophysical methods are often

Some of the most valuable engineering information available is in the detailed reports of great failures. A complete passenger train disappeared when, in 1879, all 13 main spans of the Tay railroad bridge (Scotland) collapsed, presumably because of aerostatic instability.

cheaper. The measurement of ground resistance to the passage of electricity can provide useful information; so can accurate measurement of the force of gravity. Seismic methods of survey include the analysis of the vibrations set up by an underground explosion, and shock-wave analysis under water has been used to determine the depth of rock under the mud and slime of the water bed.

Some of the most valuable engineering information available in the form of recorded experience is to be found in the reports of great failures: the collapse of the Tay railroad bridge, Scotland (1879), of the first Quebec cantilever bridge, Canada (1907), of the first suspended span of the second Quebec bridge (1917), and of the Tacoma-Narrows suspension bridge, Washington, USA (1940); the breach of the main breakwater of the port of Genoa (1955); the failure of the 16-km. pressure tunnel for water at

Sydney, Australia (1930), and of the Marshall Creek dam at Kansas, USA (1938); and many other expensive catastrophes. Some of those that concern us in the field of land transportation, and the lessons learned from them, are described in later chapters.

As for reports of successful civil engineering projects, the world's specialist libraries are stacked with them—in learned papers, journals, and books of every description. Today information science has become a cult. Provided he knows where to look for it the civil engineer today need never run short of recorded experience.

If information science is a 20th-century cult, research is a creed. To the civil engineer it has given the high-tensile steels, the high-strength concretes, and the remarkable new concrete prestressing techniques without which many of the world's newest great bridges could never have been built. It has made possible the development of soil-stabilization processes without which some of today's most recent tunnel projects might never have been attempted. It has cut the cost of highway maintenance by scientifically evaluating the durability of new formations and surfacing under varying use.

Perhaps the earliest example of original research in connection with a specific civil engineering achievement was the structural analysis of the dome of St. Peter's, Rome, commissioned in 1742 by Pope Benedict XIV when signs of weakness were observed. The findings of this investigation, published in 1743, were unique in their time, being based, not on opinion, but on scientific knowledge and reasoning.

Today, research for specific engineering projects is common enough. The systematic destruction of a prestressed-concrete bridge by overloading, the wind-tunnel testing of recent long-span suspension bridges, and the use of scale models to investigate the performance in service of proposed major concrete arch bridges are described in some detail in Chapters 4 and 5. Examples in the wider field of general civil engineering are to be found in the systematic destruction, under observation, of a steel-framed building at Witwatersrand, South Africa; in the use of wave-measuring apparatus and the construction and hydraulic testing of a huge scale model of the proposed Tema harbor, near Accra,

Ghana, before its design was finalized; and in the numerous scale models of projected dam spillways and outflow channels that are hydraulically tested to discover and cure, in advance, the possible costly effects of erosion, which may often be eliminated by comparatively simple, yet otherwise unpredictable, modifications.

Engineers of old sometimes worked on hunches—not because they were lazy but because the facts on which they could have based calculations were simply not known. Later, when the store of recorded factual information had begun to accumulate, applied mathematics suddenly became the very key to engineering design. The engineer, however, was still faced with a problem of labor. For example, the calculation of the stresses caused by a moving lorry on the various ties, struts, and beams of a continuous-truss bridge resting on four equidistant supports (this is an example of what the engineer calls a statically indeterminate structure—stresses in one of the bridge's spans affect all the others) is an irksome operation at the best of times. Make the center span longer than the other two and consider a stream of mixed traffic passing in both directions and the mathematics becomes so tedious that a team of experts might take months to verify statistically (and not estimate) the maximum possible stress to which every bridge member might be subject under every possible variation of loading.

Today, the computer can solve the problems of such calculation, completing a six months' task for a team of mathematicians in less than the time it takes to translate the problems into computer "language," feed them in, and retranslate the answers. But even today engineers do not always have enough precise information to rely completely on mathematics. For this reason scale models are often built and tested to check the results of calculations before the full-size work is put in hand.

Another reason for caution in accepting the results of empirical calculation is that we cannot always be dogmatic about the validity of even "factual" information. Steel of a certain composition may be known to have a certain strength. But what if there is an undetected flaw inside a vital steel component? The wind velocity in a certain district may be known never to have exceeded a certain figure in a hundred years. But this is no guarantee that the figure will not be exceeded tomorrow. Such uncertainties are taken care of by a simple device: Engineering calculations incorporate a "factor of safety." This means that if a bridge is designed to carry a maximum rolling load of 50,000 kg., the calculations are made for a load of, say, twice this figure. In fact, safety factors crop up everywhere. Traditional standard mild steel is deformed permanently if subjected to a tensile stress of 2500 kg/cm² or more. But the allowable working stress used for design calculations is normally only about 1500 kg/cm²—a figure controlled, in many countries, by official regulations as a built-in safety factor.

So much for the design aids. Now, in considerably more detail, we shall scan the most important department of the great web of design—that of the civil engineer's materials. Aesthetics will form a postscript.

Engineering Materials

Two events in the 19th century resulted in a revolution in civil engineering so stunning that it is hard to visualize what life would be like today had they not taken place. One was the invention, in 1824, of Portland cement; the other was the announcement, 32 years later, of Sir Henry Bessemer's process for the mass production of steel. (Though steel had been used for hundreds of years for swords and the like, it could only be made, by earlier processes, in small quantities and at relatively high cost.) To begin to appreciate contemporary road, bridge, and tunnel building technology, we must understand the main properties and potentialities of steel and concrete as we know them today.

Steel Before wrought iron was used for bridges, the bridge span record was held, from 1758, by a 117-m. timber arch at Wittingen in Germany. But in 1826 Thomas Telford built the Menai Straits wrought-iron chain-suspension bridge in Wales, with the then remarkable span of 174 m. This new record bore a subtle significance. For many hundreds of years the record had been held by arch bridges, mostly of stone, though the longest of all was of timber, as we have seen. But an arch has never since held this distinction—and never will! Moreover, though two cantilever bridges each held the record for a period, the Menai Straits

Thomas Telford's 174-m. wrought-iron chain suspension bridge over the Menai Straits, Wales, built in 1826, was the first important bridge designed to use the tensile strength of metal rather than the compressive strength of timber or masonry, making possible much greater spans.

bridge was the ancestor of a breed that has proved superior ever since, wherever span length is the major consideration. As we shall see in Chapter 4, there is one highly significant difference between the arch and the suspension span. In the former, the load is borne primarily by material in compression—in the latter by material in tension. This is the secret of steel. Before the discovery of wrought iron, mass-produced steel's immediate progenitor, there was no known material other than vegetable fiber that had any appreciable tensile strength. Suddenly the civil engineer found himself in possession of a material infinitely stronger in tension than anything he had known before.

Today there is a whole exciting range of steels from which to choose. High-tensile steels are stronger than ever before. Many of them can be accurately flame-cut and welded, making them immensely suitable for structural work. The most recent have largely eliminated steel's only serious weaknesses—susceptibility to brittle fracture (failure under impact at low temperature) and fatigue (weakening that is the result of continuing variations in applied stress).

The reaction of steel to tensile loading is vitally important to the engineer. When this material is subjected to increasing tension it is elastic, stretching and contracting in direct proportion to the applied load, up to a certain stress known as the yield point. At this stress, while retaining its ultimate strength, steel undergoes permanent deformation so that when the tension is removed it will not return to its original dimension. This plastic deformation increases as the tension is increased above the yield stress until the steel's ultimate strength is reached. At this point it is liable to fail. Mild steel has a yield stress of between 2500 and 3000 kg/cm^2, an ultimate strength of from 4400 to 5200 kg/cm^2. The allowable working stress in structural engineering, though varying according to the national controlling authority, is generally in the region of 1500 to 1600 kg/cm^2.

The strongest structural steel yet produced in quantity is probably the American T1 steel, which has a yield stress of 6280 kg/cm^2 and a commonly accepted allowable working stress of 3140 kg/cm^2. T1 steel is weldable, much more corrosion-resistant than mild steel, and proof against brittle fracture at the lowest temperatures that bridges and similar structures are likely to experience. But T1 steel is expensive and it may often be more economical to use one of the many low-alloy steels that have specifications lying between those of T1 and mild steel.

The importance of steel in contemporary civil engineering is self-evident. Throughout this book we shall find it rearing its aristocratic head on page after page. And of course it has another unobtrusive, though vitally important, existence in reinforced concrete, as we shall see.

Concrete The Romans discovered pozzolana, a volcanic deposit that sets solid when mixed with lime and water. They made considerable use of it in foundation work, even using it under water. Portland cement was first patented in England in 1824. It is generally made of powdered limestone and clay or shale, heated to about 1500°c and then finely ground. When mixed with water, it hardens and becomes strong because of its large content of anhydrous calcium silicates. This is the civil engineer's most important single material—a material that has the advantage of being plastic, even fluid, when laid, that can be pumped or poured

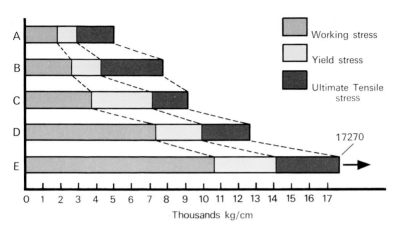

Comparison of the working strengths of various steels. Examples given are mild steel (A), low alloy metal (B), T1 steel (C), silicon manganese steel (D), and high-tensile steel wire (E). Yield stress is the point at which steel ceases to be elastic and undergoes permanent deformation; this deformation continues until the steel's ultimate strength is reached, at which point it is liable to fail.

into molds of almost any shape, and that sets solid, finally, like a lump of rock shaped to precise specifications.

Standard mass concrete is made up of a mix of Portland cement, sand, and coarse aggregate, in the proportions 1 : 2 : 4 and is normally allowed to support compressive loads up to 45 kg/cm². Very much stronger concretes can be made to support loads of up to about 400 kg/cm². The simplest method of making the material stronger is to increase the proportion of cement; but if the ratio of water to cement remains constant, the increased cement implies increased water, resulting in a mix that shrinks considerably while setting. To minimize this undesirable shrinkage the water-cement ratio has to be reduced, often well below that which makes a conveniently fluid mix. A really strong concrete mix is exceptionally dry and can be made to fill formwork of complicated shape, with a total absence of bubbles (an essential condition for strength), only by the use of powerful immersed vibrators and, possibly, by incorporating a suitable "flow" additive such as an industrial detergent.

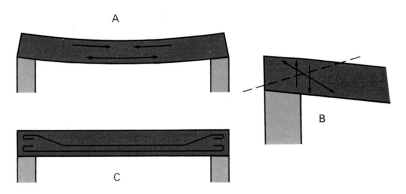

The principle of concrete reinforcement. An end-supported horizontal beam (A) has a tendency to sag and curve as shown, so that the upper half is in compression, the lower half is in tension. In addition, opposing pressures over the support cause shear stresses in the beam, resulting in diagonal tension (B). Steel reinforcement is therefore applied as shown (C) where tensile stresses will develop, concrete itself being strong enough in compression.

For special applications, where the considerable additional expense is warranted, Portland cement can be replaced by high-aluminum cement. This not only forms an inherently stronger concrete, but is rapid-hardening and (unlike Portland cement) resists corrosion from seawater and sulfates, which is sometimes a problem.

Reinforced Concrete Mass concrete is about 10 times as strong in compression as in tension. But, due to the fortunate accident that steel and concrete have almost identical constants of thermal expansion, it was discovered that steel rods could safely be set into concrete in those parts where it was required to bear tensile stresses. And by hooking the ends of the rods, still inside the concrete, the possibility of the steel "slipping" inside the concrete was eliminated. As a result of this technique satisfactory reinforced-concrete beams, slabs, and pillars could be designed to bear tensile as well as compressive forces.

The problem of where to put the reinforcement can be a complex one, but the principle should become clear if we consider the simplest of all cases, an end-supported beam bearing a single load at its center. When any horizontal beam is loaded there is a tendency for it to sag. The upper and lower surfaces consequently become slightly curved, the upper surface acquiring a radius slightly less than the lower and, therefore, becoming very slightly shorter than it was. The lower surface, in contrast, becomes a little longer. The result, in terms of stress, is compression in the upper half of the beam, tension in the lower, the maximum stresses being near the surface. In addition, the part of the beam adjacent to the support is under downward pressure, while the part directly over the support is pressed up. These two opposing pressures cause shear stresses in the beam that produce a diagonal tension, as shown in the diagram on page 22.

If our concrete beam is to withstand both the induced tensile stresses described, steel bars must be introduced where these stresses are greatest. The same basic principles of steel reinforcement apply to all forms of concrete structure—the reinforcement is introduced where tensile stresses will develop, the concrete looking after compression stresses on its own.

Prestressed Concrete   Though the constants of thermal expansion of steel and concrete are close, the modulus of elasticity of each is very different. In effect this means that when a certain tensile stress is placed on steel the material stretches by a given amount; this is not so in the case of concrete, which, if stretched, will develop cracks and possibly disintegrate.

Imagine a 250-cm.-long concrete beam reinforced, along its lower edge, with a mild-steel rod of 6.25-cm^2 cross section. If the beam is now loaded to induce a tension of 5000 kg. in the steel, the rod will stretch 0.1 cm. This is so much that it will cause cracks in the lower edge of the concrete, which will probably collapse as its compressive strength will be thereby reduced. By putting in four steel rods instead of one the induced tension of 5000 kg. will be spread over four times the area of steel, reducing the stretch (known to engineers as the strain to one quarter—only about 0.025 cm. So by putting in sufficient steel the strain can be so reduced that the concrete will not crack. Obviously, though, one of these steel rods is strong enough to withstand the 5000-kg. tension (we can allow a working stress of up to 1500 kg/cm^2), so from a strength point of view a great deal of steel is wasted when we put in sufficient steel to reduce the strain to a

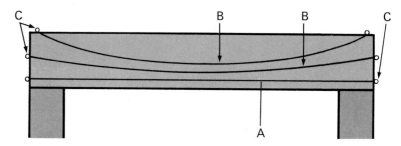

Location of steel-wire reinforcement in a typical prestressed-concrete beam. In this case high-tensile steel wires are run through straight (A) and curved (B) ducts, post-tensioned in position, and secured with anchoring devices (C). Gaps between steel and concrete are then filled with cement grout under pressure.

point well below that which will crack the concrete.

Suppose now that the steel rod inside the concrete has somehow been stretched 0.1 cm., by pulling it with a tensile force of 5000 kg., *before* the concrete is placed around it. With this "prestress" applied it will pull the concrete together, compressing it with the same force that was used to stretch the steel. When a load is placed on this prestressed beam the induced compression within it must be overcome by tension before any *additional* load will bear on the steel and so stretch it more than has been done already. It should now be clear that by this system of prestressing, far less steel is required to bear tension in reinforced concrete than with ordinary unstressed steel rods.

It all sounds very simple and the idea was, in fact, thought of as early as the late 19th century. Unfortunately, the steels available in those early days of reinforced concrete could not be stretched enough under load to make prestressing effective. The reason was a combination of several factors. Concrete shrinks slightly as it sets and cures. It also consolidates very slightly under a sustained load. Similarly steel "creeps"—that is, changes shape very slightly under sustained load. In those early days, when the quality of concrete was low, and only mild steel available, these factors combined to cancel out much of the prestress that could be applied.

It was the French engineer Eugène Freyssinet who first used high-quality concrete and high-tensile steel to make prestressed concrete. This made the technique practical for the simple reason that the steel could be so highly stressed that the total of the concrete shrinkage and the creep in both this and the steel canceled out only a very small percentage of the induced strain in the steel, leaving sufficient of the prestressing force to fulfil its designed purpose.

There are two main methods used to make prestressed concrete. In one, the steel is placed in forms and stressed, from outside, before the concrete is poured. When this sets and cures, the friction between it and the steel retains the tension in the latter after the external stressing load has been removed. In the alternative method, the concrete beam (or slab or pillar or whatever it may be) is made with hollow ducts running through it. Steel cables are passed through these ducts and "post-tensioned" after erection of the structure, suitable end fixings of various kinds being available to grip the stretched steel and bear against the concrete. As soon as the steel has been tensioned and anchored in place, the gap remaining between steel and concrete is usually filled by forcing in cement grout (thin mortar) under pressure.

A refinement made possible by post-tensioning is the placing

This 35-m. footbridge beam (two of these units making one bridge) is made of prestressed concrete and weighs 25,000 kg. The ends of the reinforcing high-tensile steel wire running through it are clearly visible.

of reinforcement steel wires along a curve, following the line of maximum tension in the loaded beam or slab. In this way a single wire, or set of wires, can be placed to prestress the concrete in such a way as to counteract tensions induced by bending and shear together, making for increased economy in both the steel and the concrete.

So efficient is modern prestressed concrete that a beam, properly designed, is said to "carry its own weight." This means that, at least in theory, the weight of a beam of this material, unlike one of steel, would never be heavier than the total load it could carry, whatever its span. There is a limit to the span of a steel beam or girder because there comes a point when the weight of the steel required to make the beam or girder longer becomes heavier than the total load it can support. This is not so with a properly designed prestressed-concrete beam.

The economies that prestressing has made possible are enormous. Only half the concrete and one third of the steel is required to build a typical bridge, compared with a similar structure designed in unprestressed reinforced concrete. And, of course, economy is not the only advantage; the architectural possibilities that this material opens up, with more slender slabs, beams, columns, and arches, are almost limitless.

Other Materials Modern aluminum alloys offer the engineer a better strength-weight ratio than some structural steels. (Mild steel has a density of about 7850 kg/m^3, whereas an aluminum alloy of equal strength weighs only 2800 kg/m^3.)

Aluminum alloys also have the great advantage of being relatively inert chemically—they do not corrode, like steel, in normal atmospheres and so require no protection, no maintenance, and no paint. Of course there is a snag—the price. But if the cost of aluminum can be lowered while that of steel continues to rise, there may come a time when, in a particular place, the cost of maintenance will decide the issue, making the aluminum alloy more economical than steel. The same may be said of stainless steel, which, as yet, is generally too expensive for the structural engineer. Though cast iron has no strength in tension, it is an excellent material in compression and does not corrode. It is commonly used in tunnel linings, where tensile stresses are minor but the compression great, and where resistance against corrosion is often vital.

Plastics now have applications in civil engineering. Glass-fiber-reinforced epoxide is being used on London's new Victoria Line Underground to seal the joints between the tunnel lining segments against underground water. Perhaps the most surprising of new civil engineering materials is PTFE, the "zero" friction compound, a form of which every housewife knows as the coating of her nonstick saucepans. A new 1.2-km. automobile flyover in Manchester, England (described in Chapter 3), has no expansion joints except at the main abutments. Expansion is allowed for by the continuous, four-lane, prestressed-concrete superstructure sliding bodily on its supporting columns. The "sliding" bearings contain a PTFE-to-stainless-steel interface. A similar use for this material is found in the bearings of an immersed-tube automobile tunnel now under construction in Amsterdam. (Some details of this will be found in Chapter 7.) Here the PTFE is in the form of disks placed between steel bearing plates. The purpose is to eliminate horizontal stresses on the foundation piles due to temperature expansion or contraction of the enormous concrete tunnel sections.

There are several other materials used regularly in different branches of transport engineering. Though concrete is being used increasingly for railroad sleepers, timber still has a place. Crushed stone is used as railroad ballast. Engineering bricks are frequently used to support the ends of bridges. Well laid, a pier of these bricks can bear a load of up to 6000 kg/cm²—four times that of common house bricks. Stone is similarly used; a granite-block pier can withstand a loading of over 7500 kg/cm². But both brickwork and masonry have the weakness of mass concrete—they cannot bear loading in tension. All these materials have special uses in specific situations.

Aesthetics

Often the cost of an aesthetically pleasing civil engineering work need be very little different from a structurally perfect visual horror. The difference arises in the temperament of the designer. The towers of the Golden Gate suspension bridge

Aesthetics overruled by economy. When O. H. Ammann designed New York's George Washington bridge he intended the steel towers to be clad in stone. The sponsors unexpectedly objected on grounds of cost, and the result was the starkly functional, but by no means unattractive, towers seen here.

appear to be sculptured in stone. They look worthy of the load they have to carry. Yet no one would doubt that they are of steel. Is this, then, a deceit? Of course not. In 1935 granite-faced buildings were fashionable and correct. To model the towers of a great bridge in the same idiom gave them an individuality that marks their place in history.

Hardly two years later the great steel arch at Sydney, Australia, was thrown across the harbor. Structurally this arch required no towers. Yet the people of Sydney agreed to a considerable sum being spent on the two granite pylons that stand at the ends of the bridge; and it is those pylons that give the bridge an unmistakable image. The people of Sydney paid a lot that their bridge might have character. No one can say they have ever been sorry.

Two more similar examples are the Brooklyn and George Washington bridges at New York, USA. The former is quite probably the most photographed bridge in the world; and the reason, apart from its being part of the city's history, lies surely in its finely proportioned massive brick towers, designed by an engineer who was, fortunately, an artist too. But what of O. H. Ammann's George Washington bridge? Here things were the other way round. Ammann intended the towers to be clad in stone. But the sponsors decided, unexpectedly, not to stand the additional cost. The result was a pair of starkly functional steel towers. By no means unattractive, they are however a typical product of their age, for the lattice girder is a type of construction we may never see again in such a structure. This bridge acquired its unique aesthetic character by an unforeseen, yet happy, chance.

Construction

Turning from design to construction, we must briefly consider three distinct areas: equipment, processes, and management. The purpose of equipment is obvious—to apply power to the job in the most economical manner. The civil engineer is concerned with two distinct types of equipment—that used in all branches of his profession, and specialized equipment. Of the second type we are only concerned here with: roadmaking plant (scrapers, road-surface-laying machines, vibrating and other rollers, some of which are described in Chapter 3); railroad plant (rail-laying equipment, ballast-cleaning and placing machines, also mentioned in Chapter 3); a few special machines used in bridge building (an example is the equipment used to "spin" the cables of suspension bridges as explained in Chapter 5); and tunneling plant (described in Chapter 6; this includes rock drills, jumbos, rock and clay shovels, shields and diggers, spoil conveyors, segment-placing machines, and ventilation equipment).

Of what we might call universal civil engineering equipment, machines for lifting, pulling, and pushing comprise one major group, represented by cranes of every description (fixed cranes, mobile cranes, tower cranes, and gantries), winches and jacks (screw and hydraulic), and in special circumstances even helicopters. A second major group consists of excavating machinery such as mechanical shovels, draglines, bulldozers, and dredgers.

Transport accounts for a wide range (from trucks and trailers of all sizes and descriptions, through small-gauge temporary railroads and aerial ropeways to freight aircraft). Finally there is an impressive range of other items, such as welding, compressed-air, and pumping plant, impact and vibrating pile drivers, and survey instruments including stereo air-survey cameras. For the reader who is interested in any of this astonishing variety of general equipment, which includes machines costing well over a million dollars, other books should be consulted.

The principal processes that concern us in this book include road- and rail-laying methods, bridge-erection techniques, and tunneling systems, all of which will be treated in the chapters directly concerned. Here I shall confine myself to a few words on two groups of processes common to all civil engineering: the modification of soil properties, which is important in many kinds of foundation work; and concreting systems.

Modification of Soil Properties

There are three main aims in modifying the properties of soils: to enable them to sustain greater loads; to reduce their tendency to fall (especially during tunneling); to render them watertight.

Apart from the natural consolidation of clay and silt, which can be accelerated by regulating the speed of building on it and by installing vertical sand drains, soil compaction can be achieved physically by rolling, ramming, pile driving, and vibrating. Loose unsaturated sand can be compacted by flooding and other loose soils by the use of explosives, which were very successfully employed, for example, during the building of the Franklin Falls dam, USA.

Chemical methods can be used to consolidate some soils. Clay, for instance, is modified by a process known as *base exchange* when common salt (sodium chloride) reacts with it chemically, replacing calcium by sodium. For example, a clay cofferdam (a watertight enclosure on sea- or riverbed from which water is pumped to allow construction) can sometimes be made more watertight by treating it with seawater. Chemical injection is also frequently used to consolidate or waterproof a soil through which a tunnel is being bored. One method is the injection of a suspension of bentonite (a form of clay). Pumped into sandy strata, this clogs the pores, greatly reducing the sand's permeability.

Excavating machinery and trucks of all kinds provide the heavy equipment of many civil engineering contracts. Here a diesel-powered dragline with a 20-m. boom and a 2.7-m³ bucket is being used to grade a bank on a freeway extension.

A number of fluid processes have been patented—for example, injection of sodium silicate and certain salts, separately, causes a reaction that precipitates silica gel.

Grouting—that is, pumping a water-cement mixture into rock fissures—has been widely used to seal off water flow during tunneling. Grouting of sandy soils is also possible with bituminous emulsions that are mixed with a coagulator as they are injected. The result is precipitation of the bitumen, which seals the interstices between the grains of sand.

When excavation work goes below the water table (that is, the upper limit of ground wholly saturated with water) it is possible to lower the water level in the region of the work so that this may proceed in the dry. This can be done by sinking tube wells around the site and pumping. Ground can also be frozen at the site of underground excavation work so that the water in it becomes ice, sealing off the fluid water around it. Though the cost of the required freezing plant is high, this method has the great advantage that it can be used at any depth; the compressed-air method, described in Chapter 5, is limited to depths up to about 30 m. below water level.

Concreting

The concrete of the south pier of the Golden Gate suspension bridge, San Francisco, USA, was poured under seawater, by pumping it down through a large-bore pipe straight into the formwork, which had been fitted by divers. More recently a convenient process has been introduced for underwater concreting. This Prepakt system, which is patented, was used extensively for the foundations of the Mackinac suspension bridge, Michigan, USA. The method is first to place broken rock (generally up to about 12 cm. in size) in the formwork under water and then to pump in a special cement-sand mix that contains a patented ingredient. This displaces the water without diluting significantly, and sets to form a good-quality concrete.

There are various concreting processes for special circumstances. For example, where an unusually strong concrete is required and the reinforcement is complex, the exceptionally dry mix that has to be used may not flow readily enough, even with extensive vibration. In such cases the addition of a quantity of industrial detergent can improve the flow properties of the mix sufficiently to make the exclusion of air bubbles a much simpler problem.

Another process, sometimes used where concreting is to be carried out in exceptionally cold weather, is the preheating by steam of the coarse aggregate and sand, and the addition of calcium chloride to the mix. The latter, reacting with some of the water in the mix, gives off the heat of the resulting chemical reaction slowly from within, keeping the concrete temperature above freezing until it has cured.

Management

Management in civil engineering is the coordination of men, machines, materials, and processes to realize design. The art of management is entirely independent of engineering but the modern management consultant can advise a civil engineering

firm as successfully as any other—it could as well be a manu-
facturer of synthetic fibers as a firm of contracting engineers—
how better to manage its affairs, how to obtain and retain the
man best qualified for a particular job, how to cut down on the
completion time for a project without disproportionate expense
on additional plant and labor, how to utilize the plant most
economically, and how to organize and carry through a whole
complex project most efficiently.

Indeed management is so much a separate technology, using
all manner of subtle techniques—work study, time and motion
study, organization and methods research, critical path analysis—
that it is clearly outside my brief to describe it here. It is sufficient
to say that experience has proved that the retention of management consultants on a large and complicated civil engineering
project can result in great savings, both direct and indirect, for
the contractor.

One word, though, about critical path analysis (CPA). This is a
comparatively new technique that, in principle, is absurdly
simple, and that any intelligent engineer can himself profitably
use even on relatively small jobs. Essentially it is a graphic method
of depicting all the interrelated activities and phases in a project
of any kind, showing exactly how each of these activities depends
(or does not depend) on the others. From the diagram (which consists
of numbered circles, denoting events in the project—e.g. foundation excavation completed—and arrows, denoting activities, the
time taken by each activity being indicated by an accompanying
figure) any man trained in the technique can identify the critical
path in the organization of the project—the one sequence of
particular events on which the time of completion is dependent.
This identification of the critical path not only enables him to
control the work with more discrimination, but in addition tells
him how to reorganize more rationally if this is possible and
economically desirable.

Many expert managers, on first learning about CPA, have
thought it so elementary as to be superfluous to an intelligent
organized mind. In fact, the system has been successfully applied
to projects so large that, not only could one man not hope to
grasp all the implications, but computers have been necessary

to ensure the fullest possible analysis and rationalization of the complex associated CPA network in time for them to be put to practical use.

A computer, however, is only needed in exceptional cases. An experienced construction engineer may state categorically that a particular bridge will take not less than, say, 12 months to build, and that labor and plant will cost not less than, perhaps, a million dollars. Yet when he draws the relevant CPA network, calculates the figures pertinent to the critical and noncritical paths, and analyzes the results in accordance with the rules of the system, he may astonish himself by discovering that, for all his experience, the technique has shown him how to cut down the project time to 10 months without increasing his costs—or how to reduce the cost substantially, perhaps without exceeding the contract time.

Welfare of labor can be an exceptional problem in civil engineering management. Works are not infrequently sited well away from centers of population; and an engineering project is essentially temporary. This may mean, therefore, the construction of a temporary labor camp and, since many civil engineering jobs take a year or more to complete, every amenity may have to be provided if the workers are to remain content and not drift away. On a large project, especially in an undeveloped area of the world, it may be necessary to provide not only a canteen and a club, but also transport facilities, a cinema, a library, or even a school.

Safety at work is another vital consideration, for men on a large engineering project often have to face danger—the danger of collapse in a tunneling operation, the possibility of falling from a great height during the construction of a bridge, or the risk of contracting caisson disease when working under high atmospheric pressure on underwater foundations (see Chapter 5). The possible causes and sources of danger on engineering works are too numerous to list here, but they must be fully considered by the engineer, and he must take adequate precautions against them.

Though a civil engineer can get on perfectly well with a good degree, it is the inquisitive mind and the ingenuity born of it that can earn for him a great reputation. When the renowned Victorian engineer Isambard Brunel was building the Royal Albert railroad bridge across the River Tamar, near Plymouth, England, in 1859, he was faced with the problem of lifting a number of 1,000,000-kg. steel trusses from the barges on which they had been assembled onto the hydraulic jacks that awaited them at the foot of the piers. Being an ingenious man, Brunel found a method that cost him nothing more than a study of the almanac and a glance at his pocket watch. He assembled the trusses with their ends overhanging the barges; these he floated into position at high tide, then moored them. As the tide ebbed, the trusses were lowered gently into position.

The moral is self-evident and needs no expanding here. For in the chapters that follow, the reader will find numerous examples of ingenuity that have saved engineers billions of dollars. The successful civil engineer need not be a genius; but if he is ingenious he may well be considered one.

2 The Planning and Design of Highways

The history of modern transport begins with the invention of the wheel, over 5000 years ago. For except in Peru, where the Incas had not discovered the wheel even as late as the 16th century, all the ancient civilizations we know of—Babylonian, Chinese, Hindu, Greek—left abundant graphic evidence, in fresco and sculpture, that they knew the wheel and used it for transport.

Evidence of the existence of early roads is less easy to find, though one record, dated about 800 B.C., describes the roads of Sargon's empire, which stretched from Babylon to the Mediterranean about 1800 years earlier. By 500 B.C. there were several well-documented highways connecting the Mediterranean with the Persian Gulf. One, which crossed the Euphrates, the Tigris, and the two Zab rivers, was described by Herodotus (484–425 B.C.) in some detail—its relay stations, its fortified hostels, its garrisons and toll gates. The desert highway connecting Babylon with Egypt, described in Isaiah XL: 3-5, is of roughly the same date, and soon after it there emerged, as a single continuous highway,

Aerial view of a classic cloverleaf freeway intersection showing clearly its one major weakness: A vehicle traveling straight through passes, in rapid succession, an exit, an entrance, another exit, and another entrance. An alternative freeway interchange is diagramed on page 44.

the great trade route from Chungking in China, via Burma, through New Delhi, Teheran, and Baghdad, and so into Europe.

Roads have played a major role in molding history, sometimes as much by their absence as by their existence. The Romans built their web of long straight roads running to some 80,000 km. so that Rome could keep in touch with its administrators through the length and breadth of the empire and deploy its armies rapidly when the need arose. William the Conqueror, however, settled the noble families who crossed the English Channel with him well away from the Roman roads. He feared rebellion and knew that highways would help rebels, while bad communications would hinder and so discourage them.

The Incas built their remarkable 16,000-km. network of roads for the same largely administrative purpose as the Romans: to facilitate the running of their empire. These roads were indeed remarkable for, unlike the mainly straight, level roads of the Romans, the Incas pushed theirs relentlessly through the South American Andes, up to heights of 5000 m. and more (above the snowline), driving tunnels through solid rock, crossing deep gorges with spectacular suspension bridges supported only by vegetable-fiber cables.

The Engineering of Roads

Unfortunately there is no record of how the pre-Roman roads were built. We can presume they were hard-surfaced, for while an earth track becomes compacted by foot and horse traffic, it cannot stand up to the wheel, which breaks up the surface. And as we do know how plentiful and skilled were the stonemasons of the early civilizations, we can say with a measure of certainty that the earliest hard roads were paved with fitted flat stones.

When we come to Roman times we find the engineering of their roads well documented. Not only was their design described in detail in contemporary writings, but they were built to last so well that the original formations of some can be seen almost intact today. One of their finest highways, the Via Appia connecting Rome with Brindisi, is typical. About 4.5 m. wide, it was built in five separate layers, and had three features to ensure drainage— the surface was cambered, it rose above ground level in the form of a low causeway, and it was flanked on each side by ditches.

The Via Appia had a wearing surface of crushed lava (plentiful in southern Italy) on a gravel core. In northern England, where stone was plentiful, the Romans surfaced their roads with fitted stone slabs. The aggregates of the base course were often mixed with lime mortar as a binder, sometimes with pozzolana, forming what was virtually a concrete bed. The Romans used cheap expendable slave labor to build their roads and, once their empire (unlike the roads) had crumbled, no administration could afford to build such fine roads—at least not until recent times.

Contemporary road technology was born in early-18th-century France when a roads authority was set up by the government in 1716 and a school for young engineers founded some years later. Indeed it was a French engineer, Pierre Tresaguet (1716–96), who designed and built the first roads that combined good engineering practice with economy. He recognized the two essentials of any lasting road: a firm dry footing protected by an impervious surface. The French lead was soon followed elsewhere in Europe, two British engineers, Telford and McAdam, achieving wide fame in road-building. Thomas Telford (1757–1834), originally a stonemason, not only laid down an excellent brief for building roads, but displayed a glimpse of things to come in his specifications for grades and bends, including horizontal and vertical transition curves. His road from Shrewsbury to Holyhead (completed in 1819 and now part of Britain's A5 highway) can hardly be surpassed today for alignment and gradient, providing as it does a top-gear highway all the way. Telford's pavement was excellently engineered, but expensive. (The word *pavement*, which in Britain has the restricted meaning of sidewalk, will be used in this book to mean the whole artificial fabric that constitutes a road.) Its foundations consisted of an 18-cm. layer of heavy stones on edge, laid on the undisturbed topsoil, and this was topped with fine binding gravel.

It was a Scotsman, John Loudon McAdam (1756–1836), who finally hit the headlines, for the simple reason that he designed a serviceable but far cheaper pavement than Telford's—a design that steadily replaced the Englishman's. McAdam designed on the basis of two simple principles. These were:

1. It is the native soil that really supports the weight of traffic;
2. Preserved in a dry state, the soil will carry any weight without sinking.

The first principle led him to dispense with Telford's heavy foundation. A dry base course, designed expressly for load-spreading, rendered it an expensive luxury. Telford's binding course, too, was a luxury, for McAdam knew that the steel-tired wheels of his day soon ground the surface of a rough stone road-way, packing the chips and grindings into the voids to form a smooth watertight surface. Like all the earlier roadmakers he retained the self-draining cambered surface.

McAdam's pavement served its purpose economically and effi-ciently until, in the early years of the 20th century, rubber tires began to replace steel. Instead of the surface being continuously ground and compacted, the rubber seemed to suck out the fine material from between the larger stones, creating a rough surface that soon broke up. A firm binder was therefore needed and the first to be used was natural tar, resulting in the immortalization of McAdam's name in the English-speaking world by the com-pound word "tarmac." All that remained in the evolution of the modern road pavement was the introduction of concrete into road design.

Despite changing emphasis and simplification in detail, road design had remained basically unaltered for many thousands of years. It was simply a continuous load-bearing weatherproof carpet making possible the movement of wheeled traffic across country, over small rivers, even—by twisting and turning—up mountains. Today the principles have remained unaltered except for one entirely new idea. What road-builders lacked for thousands of years was the modern concept of traffic engineering. It was this new science that, in the face of ever-growing highway con-gestion (150 million vehicles were estimated to populate the world's 35 million kilometers of roads in 1963), produced the great 20th-century invention, the automobile freeway—first used in Italy, then copied by Hitler as a vital military facility, to-day the urgent and only answer to the automobile age explosion.

There are thus two separate spheres of engineering that con-cern the modern builder of highways. First there is the route and

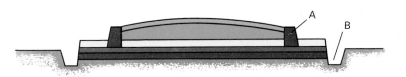

Section of a typical Roman road pavement, showing footing of compacted earth (red), waterproof course of small stones (brown), base course of Roman concrete (yellow), cambered middle course of any local hard filling (green), and wearing course (blue) of local material such as lava in Italy or stone slabs in northern England. Note also retaining stones (A) and draining ditch (B).

Tresaguet's pavement design, the precursor of the modern road. First came a 17-cm. foundation of heavy stones (red) laid on a cambered footing, followed by a 17-cm. base course of large stones (yellow) topped by an 8-cm. wearing surface of small stones (blue).

Telford's design for road pavements. This consists of a 17-cm. foundation of heavy flat stones (red) laid direct on the leveled topsoil, a two-layer cambered base course of 6-cm. stones, 50-cm. deep at the center (yellow), and a 5-cm. wearing surface of clean gravel (blue).

McAdam's simple but effective road pavement consisted of wearing surface and base course comprising three layers of 5-cm. stones laid on a compacted cambered footing.

the niceties of alignment and intersection design along that route, these being dependent as much on specifications related to safety as on the local topography. Second there is the physical specification of the road, and its construction.

Specifications relating to the safety of road users depend almost entirely on the road type, its design and purpose in particular. From this angle we can say there are five main types:
1. The rural freeway. The design criteria of this type of modern road are so stringent that old roads can rarely be satisfactorily upgraded to become freeways. Almost invariably they are planned, designed, and built from scratch.
2. The urban freeway. While having basic similarities with the rural freeway, the urban version normally has a slower design speed, and more access points tailored to local traffic conditions and requirements. The methods used for siting these roads through congested built-up areas are also necessarily very different.
3. The first-class all-purpose highway. This is usually an old road system drastically modernized with improved alignment, reduced potential traffic conflict, and a relatively high design speed.
4. The second-class rural road.
5. The downtown road.

In this book we shall concern ourselves primarily with the modern freeway, rural and urban. The technology of the other types is basically similar, though design criteria are necessarily less stringent.

Traffic Engineering

Once an authority has taken the decision to build a road and the basic type of road has been decided, the traffic engineer, who is a specialist (and who has nothing to do with the civil engineer), will lay down design specifications that are the product primarily of road safety research. Though the traffic and highway construction engineer are of different breeds, they are both, obviously, wholly concerned with roads. Therefore it is appropriate that the civil engineer knows something of the meaning of traffic engineering. What exactly does this sophisticated art comprise?

Ernest Davies, the editor of the London magazine *Traffic Engineering and Control*, has said that the function of a traffic engineer is to fit the roads to the traffic by planning and design, and the traffic to the roads by regulation and control, in order to obtain the maximum capacity with safety. Clearly it is the first half of this ingeniously comprehensive definition—the fitting of roads to existing and potential traffic needs, by planning and design—that concerns the civil engineer.

The methods used are wholly scientific, and analysis of the traffic engineer's findings enables roads engineers to design substantially safer roads than would otherwise be possible. Guesswork is no longer needed in the redesigning of existing routes and intersections, and new highways can be custom-built for safety from the start. In modern freeway design we find the quintessence of the traffic engineer's art. Here capacity is increased by high design speeds, and safety is ensured by the elimination of every circumstance in which road geometry or traffic conflict might contribute unnecessarily to the causing of accidents. For those who feel instinctively that high speeds in themselves spell potential danger, research suggests otherwise. Professor J. Carle Monagle, an American authority, has gone so far as to state that "freeways of an equal number of traffic lanes handle three times the number of cars at twice the average speed and an accident rate five times as favorable as comparable service arteries."

The general meaning of the phrase *traffic engineering* is today self-evident and the means by which it is achieved are largely common sense. Yet it is only during this century that road-builders have felt the need for such a concept in tackling the problems presented by increased and much faster road traffic.

Modern freeway design attempts to eliminate most, if not all, potential conflict. The traditional intersection has been discarded. Up and down carriageways are separated by a wide central reserve. Access points are limited in number—usually not less than 8 km. apart—so that weaving of fast traffic seeking to enter the nearside lane for exit is minimized; they are provided with acceleration lanes for incoming traffic and deceleration lanes for those leaving the freeway, so that unnecessary speed changes need not be made in the through lanes. There is no turning across in front of oncoming traffic—vehicles usually leave by a nearside slip road that leads under or over the freeway. Curves con-

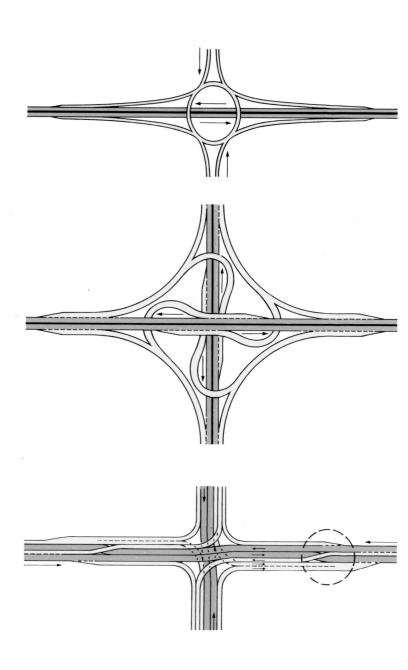

Opposite, top: raised roundabout intersection between (blue) freeway and (yellow) first-class highway (nonfreeway). The freeway exit precedes the entrance at a distance and traffic conflict is at a minimum, but the conflict inherent in any roundabout exists on the nonfreeway.

Center: catherine wheel type of freeway intersection. Full freeway interchange is provided with minimum traffic conflict (compare the classic cloverleaf interchange illustrated on page 36) but with the expense of additional over- and under-pass facilities.

Below: urban highway crossing offering minimum traffic conflict. The off-side turning lane over- or under-pass (circled) is repeated on each leg of the crossing.

form to a minimum radius and optimum superelevation, so that vehicles traveling near the freeway's design speed will negotiate the bends without any appreciable tendency to slip or sway.

The reader will probably be familiar with the general principles of contemporary freeway layout, but certain aspects of intersection design may not be too obvious.

Freeway Intersection Design

The classic cloverleaf intersection makes it possible for one freeway to cross another, with full interchange facilities, using only one major bridge. It has only one weakness: A vehicle traveling straight through passes, in rather rapid succession, an exit, an entrance, another exit, and another entrance. It is the entrance preceding an exit that can cause danger. When a freeway is to be crossed by a nonfreeway, it is advisable to avoid the situation where an entrance precedes an exit on the freeway. This is achieved most simply by the roundabout crossing diagramed on page 44. While the conflict inherent in a roundabout now exists in the nonfreeway, the freeway is as safe as is possible where full interchange facilities are provided.

In this type of intersection the roundabout can be either above or below the freeway; but an elevated roundabout has the advantage that traffic leaving the freeway enters an upgrade that assists braking from the high freeway speed; similarly vehicles entering the freeway approach on a downgrade, boosting their acceleration so that freeway speed is achieved more easily.

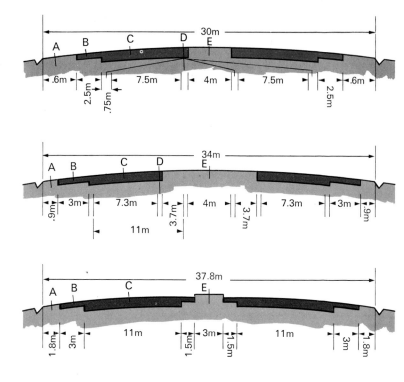

Comparison of three typical modern road designs, seen in section, showing measurement of verge (A), hard shoulder (B), carriageway (C), guide strips (D), and central reserve (E). Top: West German four-lane autobahn measuring 30-m. minimum between bridge abutments, drains, etc. Center: British four-lane motorway with provision made in the central reserve for an additional lane in each direction, the whole road having a minimum width of 34 m. Below: New Jersey Turnpike, a typical United States six-lane freeway. A 1.5-m.-wide inner hard shoulder and a minimum total width of 37.8 m. are features of this design.

Where two freeways are to cross with interchange facilities, and an alternative to the cloverleaf is sought, what may be called the *catherine wheel* interchange will avoid the cloverleaf's weak point, but at the cost of additional bridging. A compact, safe version of the catherine wheel suitable for major urban highway (nonfreeway) intersections is suggested in the diagram on page 44. Here, to save space, the off-side turning lane exits on the off side of the through lane and is carried over or under the oncoming traffic carriageway well before the intersection. With an 80 km/h speed restriction and adequate "get in lane" warning signs, this would cause no unwarranted hazard.

Study of the four intersections described will provide the reader with much food for thought. Unfortunately space does not permit us to pursue further the design problems involved.

Road Geometry

So much for traffic engineering, then. For the reader who is interested there are many excellent books dealing expertly with the subject. What the civil engineer specializing in roads needs to know is how the specifications defined by traffic engineering concern the actual designing and building of modern highways. A typical example will provide eloquent illustration; and for our example, let us consider a modern rural freeway of 110 km/h design speed, having three traffic lanes in each direction. While conditions in different countries necessarily vary and there can be no inviolable international standard, the following traffic engineer's specifications would be acceptable with minor variations in almost any country today.

Carriageway width	11 m.
Central reserve width	5 m.
Hard shoulder width	3 m.
Crossfall grade (for drainage)	1 in 40
Maximum longitudinal grade	1 in 33
Minimum radius of curves	900 m.
Superelevation for 900 m. curve	1 in 22
Uninterrupted visibility (at height 1.1 m. above road surface)	250 m.

The relevant figures may be compared with the statistics of the three typical freeways in Germany, Great Britain, and the USA, shown in the diagram on page 46. Specifications would also be laid down to control rate of change of curvature in transition from straight to curved sections and between one grade and another; also the rate of change of superelevation. The minimum headroom for overbridges would be laid down; also the minimum clear distance between piers and the off-side edge of the fast lane, and between abutments and near edge of the hard shoulder. At access points minimum lengths (depending on grades) would be specified for acceleration and deceleration lanes.

Already the road designer has a long list of stringent specifications to maintain, requiring detailed survey of the proposed route. The first aim of this survey will be to find out how, while maintaining the traffic engineer's specifications, the proposed highway can be most economically routed subject to topographical and social obstacles such as rivers, hills, forests, and townships.

One of the most expensive features of any highway designed for high automobile speeds in any but virtually flat country is that of digging cuttings and raising embankments so as not to exceed the specified maximum curvature and grades within the limits set by local physical geography. In the case of most rural freeways it is the provision of under- and over-bridges for cross traffic that pushes up the cost. For these two reasons alone a considerable amount of survey analysis must be devoted to finding the most economical route and levels. It may sometimes be cheaper to skirt round a hilly area and avoid excessive muck shifting for cuttings and embankments than to take the most direct straight route. Similarly a somewhat longer alignment may make possible the provision of adequate cross-traffic facilities with fewer or cheaper bridges.

The Caracas Autopista—a Mountain Freeway

Before we go on to the more mundane details of highway pavement design—strength requirements, the materials used, the nature of the base course and surface—a brief description of a remarkable achievement in freeway design will demonstrate how the principles we have already discussed can be applied in the most demanding circumstances.

Caracas stands about 1000 m. above sea level in the foothills of the Andes, less than 16 km., as the crow flies, from the Caribbean Sea. The capital of Venezuela, today the world's third largest petroleum producer, Caracas has had a meteoric growth, more than doubling its population between 1950 and 1960. Its only transport link with the outside world, the road to the port of La Guaira and to the international airport of Maquetia, in 1950 carried some 6000 vehicles daily along its $29\frac{1}{2}$ tortuous kilometers, and was the scene of frequent and acute traffic congestion; even when the road was clear the run took about an hour. An idea of the terrain can be drawn from the fact that 90 per cent of the road's length consisted of 395 bends, some with a radius as small as 15 m. In addition the not infrequent cyclonic storms that occur in the area sometimes caused landslides that cut the lifeline of Caracas at one stroke.

When the daunting cost of providing a more satisfactory route became less formidable than the threat to the city's very existence presented by the old road's inadequacy, six years of investigation and planning resulted in the construction, in 1950, of the Autopista. The key problem in designing the new highway lay in finding the most economical route for an 80 km/h four-lane freeway—the route that would cost least in terms of deep cuttings, high embankments, tunnels, and bridges.

The Autopista today is only 17.3 km. long, has only 36 bends with a minimum radius of 300 m., and an average grade of 1 in 20. It provides two 3.66-m. lanes in each direction (in addition to 2.5-m. shoulders and a 1.25-m. central reserve). It has two tunnels 1.8 km. and 0.4 km. long, and three prestressed-concrete arch bridges each about 150 m. long; it has cut the normal motoring time from La Guaira to Caracas to a mere 15 minutes. Many stretches of the road had to be constructed along the sides of deep ravines, necessitating a 3.66-m. drain in addition to the usual shoulder on the rising side, and a parapet as well as the shoulder on the gorge side. In deep cuttings the sides required a 6-m. paved step every 20 m. to minimize erosion, which was in any case reduced throughout by planting grass and shrubs—part of the consulting engineer designer's specifications. So many of these shrubs were needed that initial planning included the setting up of a special nursery with a capacity of 670,000 shrubs a year.

Pavement Design

It is quite impossible to standardize pavement design; there are far too many related factors: The probable loading is a complex combination of maximum truck load, tire contact pressure, the number and spacing of wheels, the density and speed of traffic; and the bearing strength of the ground can vary immensely along the route. However, experience during the past 30 years has established certain optimum specifications for both *flexible* (e.g. bituminous—for the purpose of design, a flexible pavement is

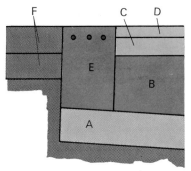

Left: typical asphalt or black-top pavement. This is made up of a base course of granular material of varying thickness (A), a 25-cm. layer of wet mix or rolled clean concrete (B), and two layers of rolled asphalt, the first 6.5 cm. (C), the second 3.5 cm. (D). Also shown are the 30-cm. guide strip and haunch made of reinforced concrete (E) and the hard shoulder of concrete and asphalt (F) designed to bear normal traffic.

Right: typical reinforced-concrete pavement. This consists of a base course of granular material of varying thickness (A), and a 30-cm. top layer of reinforced concrete (B). Also shown are the hard shoulder, consisting of an 11.5-cm. layer of granular material (C), and the 30 × 2.5 cm. guide strip of white concrete (D).

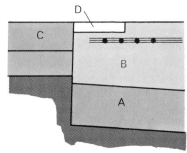

assumed to have no tensile strength) and *rigid* (concrete) pavements; these have been incorporated in an empirical method of pavement design developed by the US Army Engineers and used widely throughout the world. This is the California Bearing Ratio method (CBR). Pressure tests are made on the subsoil along the route of the planned highway, and from the results the CBR is evaluated. This is the ratio of the load required to force a standard plunger into the soil at a constant rate, to the load that would force the same plunger at the same standard rate into a standard crushed rock sample. Design charts for given materials are now used to read minimum pavement thickness against selected loading factors for given CBR values. Although the bearing strength results frequently vary widely along the route, the determined thickness derives from the lower CBR values, special treatment (e.g. strengthening of the footing) being undertaken where these drop exceptionally.

From the point of view of both design and construction a roadbed is made up of three separate elements: its footing or subgrade, its base course, and its surface or wearing course. The footing is generally the virgin soil, usually compacted by vibrating roller or other means. If the subsoil is exceptionally soft it may have to be replaced by a layer of more compact material. The base course is generally made up of whatever granular material is locally available. Ideally this would be crushed rock of a minimum depth of 15 cm., but it could equally be made of up to 60 cm. of softer material, such as colliery waste. The footing and base course may be combined, for example, by converting the top 15 cm. of the subsoil into soil cement, as explained in the following chapter.

The surface is usually either solid concrete or asphalt. A typical contemporary concrete road slab would be 30 cm. thick with a layer of mild steel mesh as reinforcement about 7.5 cm. below the surface. An alternative treatment would be 20–25 cm. of *lean* concrete (such as a 20 to 1 gravel-cement mix), this middle course being topped by 10 cm. of hot-rolled asphalt, which would probably be applied in two layers, the upper being the wearing surface. Road pavements of this type would normally have a 30-cm.-wide solid concrete haunch at each edge, right down to the footing.

On a recently built 64-km. section of the US Insterstate Route 70, the final pavement thickness is to be 56 cm., all of it asphalt based. First, laid on a compacted footing, is a 36-cm. base course comprising 62 per cent sand, 8 per cent gravel, 10 per cent crushed sandstone (1–4 cm. in size), and 20 per cent mineral filler, to which mixture was added a further $6\frac{1}{4}$ per cent asphalt. (In fact, the thicknesses varied 13 mm. either way, depending upon which of

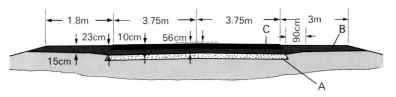

Cross section of one carriageway of a new all-asphalt section of US Route 70, showing the compacted footing (A), the asphalt base course (B), and the asphalt bearing surface (C).

two types of locally available aggregate was used in the mix.) On this base course was laid a 10-cm. layer of asphaltic concrete made up of 8 per cent sand, 41 per cent gravel, 10 per cent crushed sandstone (passing through a 2-cm. sieve), and 41 per cent fine sandstone screeings, to which was added a further $5\frac{3}{4}$ per cent asphalt. The road will be used at this thickness for some years, after which a further 10-cm. layer of asphaltic concrete will be added.

Space research would seem to have presented the road engineer with a problem, demanding as it does the transporting of loads measured in millions of kilograms. The designer's answer, however, is surprisingly simple. The first step is to use correctly designed vehicles with wheel and tire specifications ensuring even distribution of the load over the widest practical area of pavement. Only a little extra road-slab thickness is then needed to provide the extra strength. A recent British 48-wheel transporter incorporates a hovercraft-style air cushion within a flexible skirt. By evenly spreading the weight, this vehicle can safely transport 300,000-kg. loads over roads and bridges built to carry only 200,000 kg.

The Urban Freeway

Urban freeway design represents a compromise. While the aim is to eliminate all possible traffic conflict, the best design criteria of the rural freeway cannot always be maintained. For one thing, space is often limited and access points must be more frequent if the city freeway is to serve its purpose fully. Design speed is almost invariably lower, minimum curve radius less, maximum gradient higher. The principles, however, are the same.

As the city freeway is always built after the city, its route must frequently overlap or cross existing highways. There are two methods of overcoming the basic problem of pushing the freeway

Opposite: This four-lane, 16-m.-wide raised urban freeway is part of Tokyo's Expressway route No. 4 linking the Olympic Stadium with Haneda International Airport. Completed in 1964, it consists of a driveway surface of reinforced concrete 16 cm. thick, supported on hollow steel columns, and can take a live load of 5000 kg/m. Where the road is split into two directions, as in the foreground, its 8-m. width is cantilevered out from a single row of columns.

through in the face of the many obstacles, yet with a minimum dislocation of existing transportation facilities. One is to use tunnels, the other is to build elevated roads; the one may be more suitable and more economic in one situation, the other the best in another. In France, Paris now has a 20-km. tunnel for east-west rapid automobile transit. Running about 30 m. below normal street level it is provided with four surface-to-tunnel interchange stations.

The alternative—the elevated road—is today a common sight in cities around the globe. Its design is a complex engineering problem with which I shall not deal here. An example will, however, be described in Chapter 4. In practice the elevated roadway often has to be supported on narrow columns that will occupy the minimum of space below. Indeed such roads are not infrequently cantilevered out on each side of a single row of columns, steel and prestressed concrete being suitable alternative load-bearing materials. A recent development in Great Britain is the prefabricated flyover. The first, completed early in 1967, had 22 spans. Six men erected it by floodlight in eight nights; daytime traffic was not obstructed.

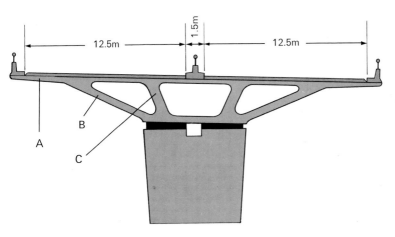

12.5m   1.5m   12.5m

A

B

C

Opposite: this close-up view of the 16-m.-wide two-way section of the Tokyo Expressway during construction shows clearly the twin continuous steel box girders supported by a double row of hollow steel columns. Above: cross section of a design for a six-lane elevated freeway in prestressed concrete cantilevered out from single columns. Use is made of longitudinal (A), transverse (B), and vertical (C) prestressing. Diagram also shows how sliding bearings (black) containing a PTFE-to-stainless-steel interface are used to provide stress adjustments and to allow for expansion movement.

Airfield Design

Although an airfield is certainly not a road, there are obviously many similarities. And since this book attempts to cover the engineering of transportation on land, the landing field of the modern airplane must have at least one mention.

There are six main factors to be taken into account in the design of airport runways:

1. They must be long enough to permit the heaviest aircraft likely to use them to become airborne comfortably in all foreseeable circumstances.

2. They must be wide enough to present a reasonable target for a pilot to land the largest aircraft on safely.

3. They must be strong enough to withstand the great weight of a modern airliner, and must be able to stand up to the hot blast of a jet engine.

4. They must have a nonskid surface, providing sufficient braking action under the worst weather conditions in which aircraft are likely to use them, for the pilot to bring his machine safely to rest without risk of skidding.

5. They must be laid out so as always to provide a landing or take-

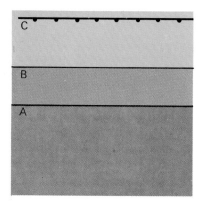

Cross section of typical runway pavement for use by supersonic jet airliners. It is made up of a base course of compacted silty clay (A), a 25-cm. layer of soil cement (B), and a 35-cm. layer of reinforced concrete (C).

off direction into—or nearly into—the prevailing wind.

6. They must provide sufficient capacity to accommodate safely all flights in and out of the airport.

The trouble about deciding the length of an airport's runway is the ever-increasing requirement of modern transport aircraft. In the mid-1930s the fastest heavy airliner flew at 290 km/h, and required a 1000-m. runway. By the early 1950s the speed had doubled, and runways had to be 2100 m. long. Today a typical commercial passenger aircraft travels at 900 km/h or more, and needs a runway 3000 m. long; the United States has laid down a runway length of 3200 m. as standard for intercontinental airports. Whether this length will suffice the jet airliners currently under development is uncertain. Their cruising speed will be in the region of Mach 3 (3200 km/h) and their weight approximately 250,000 kg. The problem of bringing an object of this weight and speed safely to rest on earth is receiving attention.

Runway width is a lesser problem. It has become standardized at about 50 m. for most modern airports, though an extra 15–20 m. is sometimes provided in unusually busy intercontinental airports.

When an aircraft has landed it has to taxi to the loading area. The taxiways are normally narrower than the runways—25 m. is a typical dimension—but of course these have to stand the same enormous weights.

Requirements of runway and taxiway strength, like runway length, have been rocketing up during the last 30 years. The heaviest aircraft in the 1930s rarely weighed above 1000 kg. Ten years later the figure had jumped to 30,000 kg. and by the late 1950s to an almost unbelievable 150,000 kg.—well in excess of the load that the modern road is designed to carry—though load-spreading by providing an increased number of spaced landing wheels prevented many existing runways becoming immediately obsolete. Now, we are told that supersonic airliners under development will weigh 250,000 kg., and though this is to be distributed over an even greater area by a whole cluster of landing wheels, worldwide design practice already specifies a runway strength sufficient to bear 100,000 kg. per single wheel or 125,000 kg. for a pair of dual wheels.

To withstand these huge concentrated pressures contemporary airport runways and taxiways are considerably stronger than the heaviest highway pavement, and the commonly held belief that steel reinforcement was uneconomic in a concrete runway has been discarded—it has been proved conclusively to lengthen its service life significantly. The methods used to design airport runway pavements, both flexible and rigid, are virtually the same as for highway pavement design; they are based on the California Bearing Ratio method referred to earlier, using especially prepared design charts based on the heaviest aircraft to be catered for.

A typical airport pavement, designed by the CBR method for use by a supersonic jet airliner weighing 200,000 kg., having land-

This star airport layout provides for two runways (each about 3.2 km. in length) with landing or takeoff direction into, or nearly into, any prevailing wind. Airport service terminal and control buildings are usually sited in the center with access by tunnel under runways. London's Heathrow airport is designed on this basic principle.

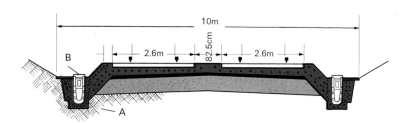

Cross section of typical railroad bed in a clay cutting, showing compacted clay base (A), the 50-cm. layer of sand or stone dust (gray), and a 5-cm. layer of stone chippings (speckled area), topped by a bed of standard stone or slag ballast (red). Also shown are the precast drainage units laid in concrete at each side (B).

ing wheels in groups of four spaced 90 cm. apart and 180 cm. one behind the other, calculated contact pressure 12.3 kg/cm², on an average Texas (USA) coast silty clay base, would have a 25-cm. subgrade of soil cement, overlaid by a 35-cm. top-reinforced concrete slab, the whole load bearing on a heavily compacted footing.

The aim of runway layout design is to provide aircraft with a landing or takeoff direction into, or nearly into, the wind. (As airliners grow faster and heavier, however, the side-wind pressure becomes relatively less of a hazard.) Current practice is generally to provide three runways at 120° to each other, providing six landing and takeoff directions. Also, because large airports are growing busier and busier, and one runway in a given direction rarely suffices, the star configuration has been adopted as an economical layout providing two runways in each direction with the minimum use of land. In some locations, where there is a steady prevailing wind, a single-direction runway may suffice, as in Hong Kong, where airliners land on a causeway built out into the bay.

The runways of a modern airport present the consulting engineer with a comparatively simple problem. There are no grades or bends, and there is no superelevation to consider. Their strength, on the other hand, must be formidable, and they present a substantial construction task; typically there would be 20 km. of roadbed, four or five times as wide as a major three-lane automobile carriageway, with a considerably greater bearing strength.

The Railroad Bed

Since railroad tracklaying is a specialist engineering function, railroad engineering has itself tended to become a wholly specialist branch of civil engineering. The principles involved in railroad bridge building, tunneling, and formation preparation do, of course, follow normal engineering practice. The survey and planning of a railroad line is not unlike that of a rural freeway. The object is to provide the most economical route in terms of earthmoving, bridging, and tunneling, within the limits laid by maximum grade and minimum radius specifications. Wherever possible the volume of excavated earth must balance that put into embankments if economy is to be achieved. This applies laterally (as when preparing a formation along a slope) as well as longitudinally.

The principal design feature of a railroad bed is the provision of a ballast bed that will spread the very heavy loads involved (with the aid, of course, of the comparatively stiff steel rails and closely spaced sleepers, themselves designed for load-spreading) so that the bearing strength of the ground below will not be exceeded.

A typical heavy railroad formation consists of a 25-cm. layer of stone or slag ballast (graded evenly from 2 to 5 cm.) spread directly on compacted soil. When the sleepers—which nowadays may be of prestressed concrete—have been laid, the gaps between them are then filled with more ballast. With this simple formation most soils, well compacted, will withstand the impact loading of fast heavy railroad traffic. The bearing capacity of clay, however, is so reduced when wet that a 15- to 30-cm. blanket of sand or ashes must be placed between the clay and the ballast. This prevents wet clay creeping up into the ballast and clogging it, thereby reducing its load-spreading capacity.

3 Road Construction

Once the alignment of a new highway has been determined and its specifications settled, the necessary land must be acquired. Sometimes, where local owners are insensible to community needs, this proves to be a lengthy and costly process, requiring considerable government powers and often involving frustrating legal delaying actions. When all this preliminary wrangling has been completed, the road construction engineer gives a sigh of relief and sets to work to build the highway. So far as he is concerned there are four distinct operations:

1. Bridge and tunnel construction.
2. Excavation, filling, and preparation of the footing, generally accompanied by drainage works and fencing.
3. Construction of the pavement.
4. Finishing, which comprises a multitude of minor works, such as laying footpaths, making hard shoulders, signposting, seeding grass in central and side reservations, and amenity treatment (which may include the planting of trees and shrubs).

A German slipform paver at work on a highway in France. This self-powered machine, running on caterpillar tracks, incorporates vibrating, tamping, and screeding equipment, and as it goes along extrudes a complete finished concrete slab, like toothpaste coming out of a huge flat-nozzled tube.

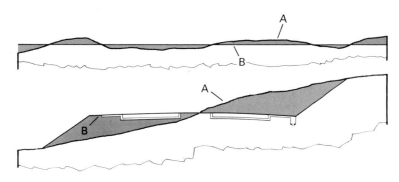

The importance of balancing cut and fill in preparing a roadbed. Top: longitudinal section of highway level in undulating country, showing original ground level (A) and road level (B). Ideally, cut (gray) should equal fill (red). Below: transverse section of roadbed on sloping ground. Here again, for engineering economy, cut and fill should cancel each other out.

Of these four operations the last is nonspecialist, and is outside the scope of this book. The first will be dealt with in later chapters; all that needs to be said here is that the building of bridges and tunnels will usually have to be started first if they are to be ready in time.

Preparation of the Roadbed

There is nothing mysterious about the actual building of a modern road. It has become a routine, mechanized of course, with variations depending on the local topography, the nature of the subsoil, the decision to surface with concrete or asphalt, and the particular machines selected (or available) for the job. The following is one possible variation of the total process; it may be taken as fairly typical of contemporary freeway construction.

The topsoil is first stripped and placed to one side in convenient heaps. It will be needed later for soiling the central reservation and verges where grass will be grown. The first machine used will probably be a tractor-drawn scraper; a row of steel teeth is dragged through the soil, cutting down about 15 cm., while a following blade, set at an angle, pushes the loosened earth to one side. A bulldozer will probably follow the scraper, collecting the earth into suitable heaps where it will not be in the way.

The entire area that the finished road and its associated reserva-tion, shoulders, and verges will cover is next cut to the designed levels, curvature, and grades. The overall plan, in the detailed design, will have been to balance exactly the "cut" with the "fill," both laterally and longitudinally, so that there will be no surplus of excavated material to dispose of and no *shortfall* (missing material) to find.

This balance may not always be possible, or may not always prove to be exact; but it is not difficult to accommodate a small surplus in landscaping, and a minor shortfall may similarly be found by shallow excavation, also incorporated in the landscaping, or possibly worked into the drainage system. Economics requires that all excavated material should be moved the minimum possible distance. This is vital. Many thousands of metric tons will be in-volved and its movement can be so costly that wasted effort could be crippling.

Machinery used for preparation of the footing will vary with the nature of the terrain and the subsoil. It could include any of the many forms of mechanical excavator, rock-ripping crawler tractors, bulldozers, dumpers, scrapers, as well as heavy or vib-rating rollers. The excavation, filling, and preparation of the footing require highly efficient organization and utilization of plant. The machines are often extremely costly and, while skillful, economic use will pay off, any inefficiency will be heavily paid for.

The levels to which the previous process will have been worked depend on the nature of the base course. If the excavation work has lifted sufficient rock for this to be crushed and used for the base course, the cut level will necessarily be some 50 cm. or more below the planned final road level, and the broken rock will then be spread and rolled in to the designed depth. The same level will be worked to if a lean concrete base course is to be laid. But if the base course is to be prepared by the process of soil stabilization, the preliminary process will not go so deep, the level worked to being the top, and not the bottom, of the base course. This is because soil stabilization is a process that creates the base course by increasing the bearing strength of the existing subsoil, rather than by replacing it with some other material; it is a process that consists of mixing a given percentage of a stabilizing agent—which may be cement, bitumen, or some other substances—with the soil. How it works and how it is carried out we shall shortly see.

The final step is the laying of the road surface, either flexible black-top pavement, or rigid reinforced concrete slab.

Soil Stabilization

Soil mechanics is a complex science. Many factors are involved in the bearing strength of soils—the nature and size of the particles, the ratios of air and water to solid matter, the percentage of organic matter, and others. Here we shall have to confine ourselves to one important factor: the range and distribution of particle sizes.

The engineer has classified soils into four principal groups according to particle size: gravel (comprising particles from 60 mm. down to 2 mm.); sand (from 2 mm. to 0.06 mm.); silt (0.06 mm. to 0.002 mm.); and clay (which includes all particles smaller than 0.002 mm.). But soils rarely consist of just one or other of these groups. Usually there is a mixture resulting in indeterminate compound names such as sandy silt, or sandy clay.

In fact it is not so much the percentages of the different-sized particles that concern the engineer as what he calls the *grading*. A soil may be either well graded, uniformly graded, or poorly graded. A well graded soil has a particle size distribution extending evenly over a wide range of sizes without an excess or deficiency of any particular size.

A uniformly graded soil, on the other hand, is one having a high percentage of one certain size of particle and a low percentage of all other sizes. A poorly graded soil is one containing, within the total range of its particle size, a relative excess of some sizes and a deficiency of others.

The word "poor" used here is a clue to the relative bearing strength of this last category of soil, for it is the poorly graded soil that generally exhibits weakness, the reason being that the voids between the particles of the size existing in excess are not sufficiently filled by the next smaller sized particles. The result is a soil that contains more water and air than is desirable and that will not readily compact. The addition of a stabilizing agent

Preparing a freeway roadbed for black-top paving by means of the soil cement stabilization technique. Here a truck is spreading cement in windrowed natural sand. The cement will then be mixed with the sand, watered, tamped, and thoroughly rolled. Finally the surface will be topped with an oil curing seal before asphalt is laid. Bearing strengths of up to 300 kg/cm² may be achieved by adding 10 per cent cement to well-graded granular soils.

to a poorly graded soil has comparatively little effect unless material having the missing particle sizes is added, and the whole mixture thoroughly compacted. (In contrast, the bearing strength of a well graded soil can be considerably increased by mechanical compaction alone.)

Once its limitations are understood, soil cement (another term for stabilized soil) can be effective as a road pavement base course. Bearing strengths as high as 300 kg/cm² have been recorded by adding 10 per cent cement to well graded natural gravel-sand-clay mixtures, and strengths of 100 kg/cm² are relatively easily achieved.

Soil stabilization can be carried out by means of conventional earth-moving equipment. First the upper layer of subsoil is loosened and pushed aside into ridges or windrows, using a blade grader. Cement, bitumen, or whatever stabilizing agent has been chosen, is then distributed along the windrows; a second pass of the grader mixes the agent into the stripped subsoil and returns the mixture to the soil's original position, where it is consolidated by roller and usually waterproofed with a sprayed coat of bitumen emulsion.

In recent years a considerable number of especially designed machines have become available for on-site soil-cement preparation. These include tractor-drawn cement spreaders that measure and distribute cement evenly and accurately onto the prepared subsoil surface; rotary tillers, also tractor-drawn, that dig 15–30 cm. into the surface and thoroughly mix the broken soil with the cement and, where necessary, with water (or alternatively spray and mix in a bitumen stabilizer); and vibrating rollers that reconsolidate the surface. More sophisticated one-pass self-powered machines carry out the entire process; stripping the surface, mixing cement or bitumen into the broken soil, then consolidating the mixture by means of multiple tampers or a rear-mounted vibrating roller. A typical large "mix-in-place" soil-stabilizing machine of this type handles up to 400,000 kg. of soil per hour, working a strip 3.75 m. wide to a depth of 20 cm. Powered by a 195-KW. diesel engine, this machine incorporates a water pump of 900 liters/min capacity and a bitumen pump delivering about 600 l/min. Maximum working speed is around 10m/min.

Laying the Base Course

Where a lean concrete or asphaltic base course is to be laid, the normal procedure is to weigh and mix the materials at one or more strategically placed batching and mixing plants. Especially designed tip trucks then dump the mixture onto the prepared footing for spreading and compaction by a machine that straddles the roadbed. A vibrating roller finishes the job.

A recent newcomer to roadmaking machinery is an automatic paver that spreads and tamps a continuous slab of lean concrete up to 30 cm. thick and 5 m. wide, handling 300,000 kg. of material an hour. This machine is steered by hand through electromagnetic clutches, but pavement grade and crossfall are controlled electronically by sensors running along taut wires, surveyed accurately into position, one on each side of the roadbed. Tip trucks feed ready-mixed concrete into the roadbed directly ahead of the paver.

Black-top Paving

Machines for automatic asphalt paving are commonplace. Most of them work in a similar manner to the concrete paver described above, evenly spreading the asphalt mix, supplied ahead by tip truck, to a predetermined thickness over the base course, ready for rolling. While asphalt surfacing is normally done in several layers of differing composition, the machine described in the previous section can lay and consolidate a 20-cm. asphalt layer in one pass producing a finished black-top pavement requiring no further treatment. Grade and crossfall are controlled electronically, as already described.

The Construction of Concrete Pavements

Concrete pavements can be constructed in many ways, but contemporary practice leans toward continuous one-pass mechanized operation, a series of machines passing along the line of the roadway, each carrying out a specific process; the whole complicated caravan is termed a *concrete train*. It is rather like a factory from one end of which the product—a continuous reinforced concrete slab—emerges. Instead of a conveyor belt passing the slab along the assembly line, however, it is the assembly line that moves, leaving the finished slab behind as it goes.

There are five separate processes in the manufacture of a concrete pavement:
1. Laying formwork and guide rails on the prepared footing or base course;
2. Batching and mixing the concrete;
3. Laying and consolidating the concrete with or without the incorporation of steel reinforcement;
4. Finishing the pavement surface;
5. Providing the necessary joints.

On the precision with which the guide rails and formwork are placed will depend the accuracy of the configuration of the finished road surface—its grade, its crossfall, its superelevation, its curves. The rails will carry the heavy plant of the concrete train and must be supported on a firm, if temporary, foundation. The formwork will provide the edges to the concrete slab while it is setting. Formwork and guide rails are sometimes combined.

Stockpiling of the materials and batch weighing of the cement and various aggregates must necessarily be carried out at suitable locations along the roadway, their selection being made for maximum economy of transportation. Concrete mixing may be done

Black-top paving machine at work evenly spreading the asphalt mix, supplied ahead by tip truck, to predetermined thickness over the base course ready for rolling. Surfacing of this kind is normally done in several layers, though one-pass asphalt pavers are also used.

centrally at the batching locations, the wet mix being taken for laying by especially designed tip trucks. Alternatively there are paving-mixers that run in the van of the concrete train, mixing and pouring the concrete on the spot. These machines incorporate means for efficient spreading of the concrete between the forms; where ready-mixed concrete is supplied by truck, this is tipped from one side into a spreader, which distributes the concrete evenly across the roadbed.

There are two commonly used methods of laying the slab, incorporating the reinforcement, and providing the necessary compaction. In the first the concrete is laid in two layers, the first up to a level about 15 per cent above the designed level of the reinforcement (the level will have dropped about this much on completion of compaction), and the second layer following after placing of the steel reinforcement mats by special handling gear that lifts them, a sheet at a time, from a trailer drawn by the spreader or paver-mixer. Where the reinforcement mats meet they are overlapped and wired together. Once the second layer of concrete is in place (and it must be added within 20 minutes of the lower layer to ensure a proper bond), compaction is carried out by means of a battery of "poker" vibrators pushed down into the wet mix. Alternatively, "pan" vibrators can be used to impart vibration through the surface of the concrete.

In the second method sufficient concrete for the entire slab is spread in one operation, the reinforcement mats being placed on top and forced down through the wet concrete to the correct level by a "mesh-placer," before compaction takes place.

Mechanical finishing is usually carried out by a machine carrying two transverse vibrating metal strips or *screeds*, each of which runs over the surface carrying a slight wave of excess mix before it, and leaving, after the second screed has passed, an almost perfectly flat surface. Some finishing machines also carry, after the screeds, a longitudinal float that traverses from side to side as it is drawn slowly forward. Any minor irregularities that still remain are now removed by means of conventional straight edges manipulated by hand from a traveling bridge. Finally the pavement is given either a burlap drag or a mechanical brush finish, to provide it with a nonskid surface.

Various forms of joints are employed in making concrete pavements. There are three basic kinds: expansion joints, contraction joints, and construction joints.

Expansion joints are normally placed across the pavement at regular intervals to allow for longitudinal expansion and contraction of the slab caused by temperature changes. Such joints are often made by laying a vertical expansion filler strip across the roadbed between the forms, before the concrete is laid. As no concrete whatsoever must bridge the gap, these strips are best laid in a shallow groove made in the roadbed footing. This prevents concrete flowing under. The filler strip rises to within 2 cm. of the finished concrete surface, being topped by a greased cap that is removed as soon as the concrete has set. The resulting groove is later cleaned and filled with a waterproof sealing compound. Expansion joints are sometimes made by cutting the concrete after it has set but before it has cured, by means of a small mobile machine having an abrasive circular saw that cuts downward into the slab.

Contraction joints are often placed both transversely at regular intervals (5 m. is a normal spacing) and along the center line of the slab. Their purpose is to channel into straight lines at known locations the fine, otherwise irregular, cracks that appear in any large slabs when the concrete sets and contracts. These joints are made either by incorporating a narrow vertical bitumenized strip in the upper part of the concrete while the slab is being made, or by the type of abrasive saw already described. The depth of transverse contraction joints is generally $\frac{1}{6}$ slab thickness, of longitudinal joints $\frac{1}{4}$ slab thickness. After the saw cutting, the slots are cleaned and filled with sealing compound.

Construction joints become necessary between the end of one day's work and the beginning of the next; also on wide pavements, such as four-lane highways and airport runways, between adjoining slabs. In the case of longitudinal construction joints, load transfer across the joint is secured by the incorporation of a tongue-and-groove overlap. A strip is added to the formwork of the first slab laid, to form a substantial groove in the edge of the slab. When the adjoining slab is poured alongside, the fresh concrete is vibrated into the goove, forming a tongue. Steel tie-bars are usually fitted to tie the joint together.

With the exception of the tongue-and-groove method used in longitudinal construction joints, load transfer at joints is usually provided for by the inclusion of steel dowels. These thick pins are embedded horizontally in one slab, and fit into greased sleeves cast into the adjoining slab. The sliding fit permits expansion and contraction movements at joints, yet transfers part of a load near the edge of one slab into the other, avoiding shearing at the joint, or other failure.

Opposite: a typical concrete train at work. In the distance a conveyor is unloading the first layer of concrete, which is then distributed by a screw spreader and compacted by a battery of poker vibrators. Next, steel-mesh reinforcement (seen at extreme right) is laid down, followed by the top layer of concrete. This too is spread by a screw spreader, and is compacted in this case by the vibrating beam machine in the center of the picture. In the foreground, the articulated finisher gives a final surface that is provided with a skid-resistant finish by means of transverse manual brushing. The concrete is finally protected by the application of a curing membrane and lengths of waterproof tenting.

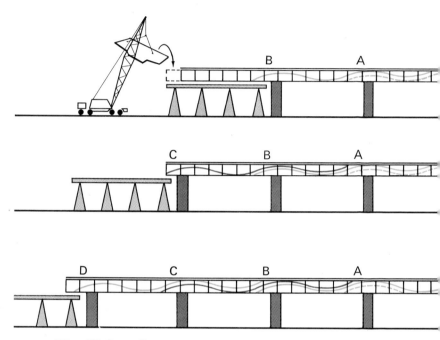

The Slipform Paver

One of the more recent additions to the growing family of road-making machines is the slipform paver, developed in the United States and illustrated on page 60. This remarkable piece of self-powered equipment running on caterpillar tracks does away with the expensive chore of laying guide rails and formwork. It incorporates vibrating, tamping, and screeding equipment so efficient that it extrudes, as it moves along, a complete finished concrete slab, rather like toothpaste coming out of a huge flat-nozzled tube. The concrete is so well compacted that the edges of the slab are fully self-supporting from the moment the slab emerges; hence the absence of formwork. The machine is even more completely electronically controlled than the paver described earlier. Two guide wires are utilized to control not only the longitudinal grade and crossfall of the extruded slab, but also the direction of the machine. The working speed of the slipform paver is a little over 2m/min while forming a 7.8 m. by 30 cm. slab, which com-

*Opposite: method used for erecting and post-tensioning prefabricated
prestressed-concrete sections of the Mancunian Way, Manchester, England. Top:
section BC being laid on staging and jointed. Center: cable between ABC (red)
installed and stressed, and staging moved on to the next section. Bottom:
cable linking BCD (blue) installed and stressed, and staging moved on to next
section. (Note that, for clarity, only seven sections are shown in each span; in
fact there were 14.) Above: a completed section of the Mancunian Way showing
the prestressed-concrete sections.*

pares favorably with the 0.75 m/min rate usually achieved with
a concrete train.

While the slipform paver was initially designed for the building
of unreinforced pavements, a method of incorporating conventional steel reinforcement in the extruded slab has been successfully devised. The mats are laid and wired together ahead of the
machine, supported at the correct height by wire slings, the
machine operating over them. The vertical "poker" or "spud"
vibrators incorporated in the paver have been found suitable for
compacting the entire slab through the steel mesh. This machine
thus replaces all the equipment of the conventional concrete
train except for the reinforcement carrier and handling gear.

Elevated Roadways

I had a word or two to say in the previous chapter on the
design of elevated roadways. While the building of these is
basically a short-span bridging operation, techniques are being

evolved that are in some respects peculiar to the specific application and so deserve mention here. The following is a description of just one such example. Others, in the main, are variations on a theme.

The three-lane two-carriageway elevated section of the Mancunian Way—the urban freeway that now runs across the southern limits of Manchester, a British industrial city—consists of two parallel 11-m. roadways, each balanced on a row of single columns. Each roadway was built up of 2.2-m.-thick prefabricated slices of prestressed concrete construction. Once the piers had been completed the erection procedure was as follows:

1. Fourteen slices (making one complete 31.5-m. span) were placed side by side on temporary staging as shown in the diagram on page 72. The 75-mm. gaps between these sections were next filled with concrete keyed into the adjoining surfaces.

2. Longitudinal prestressing cables, ABC (depicted in red), were now threaded through holes provided in the webs of the sections, and stressed from points A (top of roadway) and C (bottom of roadway). As a result the new length of roadway BC was made self-supporting (though it could not yet carry much more than its own weight). The staging was moved along the span.

3. Stages 1 and 2 were now repeated. When prestressing had been applied to section CD by means of cables BCD (depicted in blue) this section in turn became self-supporting. And, as will be seen from the diagram, section BC now had twice the original prestressing, due to the overlapping of cables ABC (red) and BCD (blue). Section BC of the roadway was now not only self-supporting, but up to full design strength for the calculated traffic loading.

An intriguing feature of the Mancunian Way elevated section is the nature of its bearings. An entire 1.2-km. length of the roadway is fixed rigidly to its supporting columns only at a central point. At all other columns the roadway rests on sliding PTFE-to-stainless-steel bearings permitting longitudinal expansion that, at the ends of the roadway, can be as much as 20 cm.—allowed for by the inclusion of comb joints in the pavement. Side guides are provided at every fifth supporting column to prevent the roadway slipping transversely off center.

Under the PTFE sliding bearings are rubber-in-steel compression bearings (carrying up to 550,000 kg. each) that permit rotation to allow for minor stress adjustments and distortion caused by heavy traffic flow. These bearings consist of large shallow steel cylinders attached to the columns, with flat steel "pistons" inside them, the roadway being supported (via the PTFE bearings) by these pistons. The space inside the cylinders, under the pistons, is filled with a natural rubber compound that acts as a viscous fluid, transferring the load hydraulically to the bottom of the cylinders, yet permitting rotation.

Runway and Railroad Construction

The experienced road construction engineer finds no problem in constructing modern airport runways. The methods employed are basically identical with those for building highways, whether black-top or concrete. The only real difference lies in the exceptional width of runway pavements, a feature taken care of by using the longitudinal construction joint between adjoining concrete slabs, or by merely marrying asphalt strips together. As for the superior strength of the modern international airport runway, this is purely a matter of correct pavement design.

When it comes to laying a permanent way, we have entered a very different field, which is really outside the scope of this book. For this is a specific expertise carried out by a specializing railroad engineer using custom-designed machines. Even modern track specifications are unfamiliar to the nonspecialist civil engineer, for railroad engineering has recently entered an explosion of change—with, for instance, prestressed concrete sleepers and continuous welded rails taking the place of the time-honored timber sleepers and jointed rails. All manner of ingenious machines have been devised for track laying, ballast laying and tamping, automatic track geometry recording, and so on, and new techniques have been developed, such as the prefabricated track junction that can be installed overnight, complete, at a busy station, so that normal traffic is in no way disrupted.

4 The Design of Great Bridges

An engineer has been commissioned to design a bridge. He knows the distance to be crossed, the problems of the approaches, the load the bridge will have to carry, the minimum span and height required for traffic under the bridge. He has investigated the physical nature of the site (including, perhaps, a deeply silted river bed); the bearing strength of the ground; the depth of firm rock; the limits of possible pressure from wind, snow, and ice; temperature limits (he must allow for expansion effects, and may be faced with a problem of cold-weather concreting); the possibility of earthquakes. He has studied the geographical situation—the availability of materials and equipment, of workshop facilities, the local transport problem. Let us say he has collected all the information he requires. How does he set about his task?

Before the engineer can prepare even a preliminary design, he must make four basic decisions. These concern:
1. The type of bridge;
2. The materials of which it will be made;

Unusually lightweight steel towers, diagonal hangers, and a hollow steel bridge deck designed like a continuous aerofoil are features of Britain's 1080-m. bridge over the Severn near Bristol, opened in 1966. Its elegant, economic design may well set a new fashion among 20th-century suspension bridges.

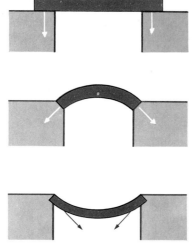

The essential technical difference between the three fundamental types of bridge lies in the form of their load-bearing structure in relation to the force of gravity. The beam bridge (top) is horizontally self-supporting and exerts only a vertical downward thrust on its piers. The feet of the arch bridge (center) tend to open under load, adding an outward horizontal component to the downward thrust. The cable of the suspension bridge (bottom) is in tension, pulling downward and inward at its supports.

3. The type of foundations that will support the bridge;
4. The construction method to be used.

On these decisions all else will depend, and in particular the cost of the bridge. Someone will have to pay the bill.

Bridge Types

There are three fundamental types of bridge, depending on the form of its load-bearing structure; its shape can be basically flat, convex, or concave. Engineers think of these as beam, arch, and suspension bridges. The diagrams on this page show clearly the essential technical difference between these three types—that is, the direction of the forces they exert on their foundations. The beam is horizontally self-supporting; it exerts mainly a vertical downward thrust on its piers (though in the event of a train or other heavy load braking suddenly on the bridge, piers, and abutments will be subject to a considerable horizontal thrust which the designer must take into account). The feet of an arch tend to open under load, adding an outward horizontal component to the downward thrust. The cable of the suspension bridge is in tension, and pulls downward and inward at its supports. In practice few bridges are so simple.

Beam Bridges There are two main types of beam bridges—the simple beam, supported at or near its ends; and the cantilever, a beam that substantially overhangs its main supports. There are variations of both kinds of beam, the commonest being the truss, a construction of linked triangles (various forms being used) that

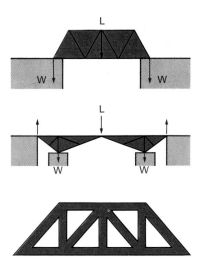

The two main types of beam bridge. The simple beam (top) is supported at or near its ends, while the cantilever (center) is a beam that substantially overhangs its main supports. The cantilever provides a means of making beam bridges considerably greater in span. A truss bridge (bottom) may be thought of as a thin beam with all unnecessary material cut away.

may be thought of as a beam in the form of a vertical slab lightened by cutting away those parts that play little or no part in giving it strength.

While beam bridges of both types exert a vertical downward thrust (W) on their main supports, the cantilever, due to its inherent tendency to pivot when the overhang is loaded, exerts an additional upward thrust at its other end. The piers of both types of beam normally have to support vertical forces only, and are therefore comparatively simple in theoretical design; but the forces within a beam vary in its different parts, and include both thrust and tension.

The first diagram on page 80 represents a beam bending under its load (L), which includes both its own dead weight and the "live" load it is designed to carry. Due to the induced curvature the lower edge becomes longer, the upper edge shorter, causing respectively tension and thrust. In the case of a box girder or truss there would be compression in the upper chord, tension in the lower. The stresses in the other members also vary according to the design and use of the truss.

In a cantilever (second diagram) the overhanging arm tends to bend down under load, causing forces opposite to those in the end-supported beam—thrust in the lower chord, tension in the upper.

Clearly the material used in a beam bridge must be capable of withstanding both tension and thrust. This is a design disadvantage not shared, as we shall see, by arches and suspension cables. The simple beam is found, in practice, to provide the most eco-

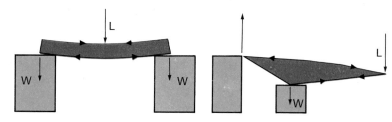

Beam and cantilever bridges under load. Both types exert vertical downward thrust (W) on their main supports. The difference is that while the beam (left) curves under load (L) so that its upper edge is in compression and lower edge in tension, in the cantilever (right) the forces are reversed, since the overhanging arm bends down under load, causing tension in the upper chord and compression in the lower.

nomical form of bridge where the span is small—up to about 45 m. Where a larger gap is to be bridged and piers will not be too costly, a multispan beam bridge is often the engineer's prescription. At Hotseh, in the Hwang Ho valley, China, stands the world's longest trestle and beam structure, 144 km. from end to end. More impressive, if not so long, is the 37 km. automobile bridge across the Pontchartrain Lake in Louisiana, USA, completed in 1956. This multispan bridge of simple beam units has 2170 short spans.

The cantilever provides a means to make beam bridges of considerably greater span, and there was a period in the history of bridge building when the steel cantilever was not only in fashion but held the long-span record. Today the cantilever has many forms and uses, but long cantilever spans do not often appear to meet contemporary requirements. The arch, which is as strong, avoids the complication of girder members in tension and can bridge wider gaps; where the live loading is not excessive the suspension span provides a more economical long-span bridge, and meets today's automobile age requirements at less expense.

A bridge with both simple beam spans and cantilevers would classify as a beam bridge, though composite in nature. A fine example is the 4.5-km. Tappan Zee bridge (built in 1955), which carries the New York Thruway over the Hudson River. The navigation channel is bridged by a 404-m. steel cantilever span (the world's sixth largest), allowing 50-m. above-water clearance. The rest of this long bridge is contructed of simple beams.

There are occasions when a long continuous beam is supported at intervals along its length: This makes it, in effect, a compound beam-cum-cantilever. A bridge built over the Sava River at Belgrade, Yugoslavia, in 1957 is a fine example of this type of construction. It has a clear span (the record for a box girder) of 257 m. and two anchor spans, each of 74 m.

Arch Bridges The abutments of arch bridges have to withstand the outward horizontal component of the arch's angular thrust as well as the simple downward vertical load borne by beam bridge piers. They are therefore of more complex design and consequently more costly. Unlike the beam, however, which itself must withstand tensile as well as compressive forces, a true arch is in a state of compression throughout. It can therefore be built of materials that, though strong in compression, are weak in tension.

The roadway of an arch bridge may be supported above the arch or suspended below it. The arch itself may be "hinged," which means it is pin mounted at its ends (the two-hinged arch) and possibly at the crown too (making a three-hinged arch); or it

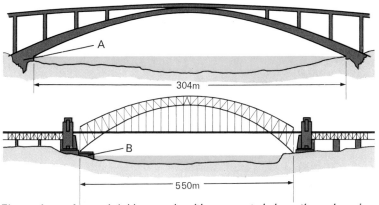

The roadway of an arch bridge may be either supported above the arch, as in the case of the concrete Gladesville bridge, Sydney (top), or suspended below it, as in the older trussed steel Sydney Harbor bridge (below). In both cases the abutments (A and B) must withstand the outward horizontal component of the arch's thrust as well as a downward vertical load.

can be monolithic with its abutments, and therefore hingeless (see diagram on page 81). A true arch is built as a circle or parabola; but it can also be a "portal"—made up of rigidly joined straight or nearly straight sections. (The Grand Duchess Charlotte Bridge, Luxembourg, span 230 m., is an excellent example, completed in 1965.) It may be "trussed," having separate top and bottom chords joined by cross members; and it may be "tied," its two ends connected by a horizontal member that, acting in tension, bears the full horizontal component of the arch's angular thrust, so that the force acting on the foundations is vertical only, as in the case of a simple beam.

Inherent features of the arch are its rigidity and strength. It is easy to erect where temporary falsework can be built; but the situation that calls for a long arch bridge—the situation where intermediate piers are for some reason impracticable—often means that falsework is impracticable too. In fact the long arch often confronts the engineer with unusual erection problems and must frequently be designed to withstand stresses during erection that it will never have to bear when complete.

Suspension Bridges While simple suspension bridges exist in primitive forms, most modern bridges of this type have their cables supported by towers that are stayed, usually by a continuation of the main cables. The inward and downward pull of the simple suspension bridge is thus converted into downward thrust in the towers and upward angular tension in the stays.

The foundations of this type of bridge consist of two elements: piers for the towers and tension anchorages for the stays. The roadway is suspended from the main cables, which fall in a catenary curve—that is, a curve of the type formed, due to its own weight, by a chain suspended by both ends. A fourth essential element, not so obvious, is longitudinal stiffening of the deck, usually achieved by the incorporation of a long, slender, continuous truss either below or beside the road deck. If this stiffening is not provided, a moving live load will tend to form a wave along the deck as it passes and lateral winds may cause dangerous swaying and other oscillations.

There are two variations of this type of bridge. By incorporating a long strut between the ends of the stays, the opposing

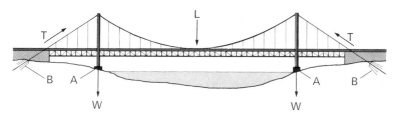

Typical design of a modern suspension bridge, showing how inward and downward pull (L) is converted into a vertical downward thrust (W) in the towers, and upward angular tension (T) in the stays. The foundations consist of piers for the towers (A) under compressive stress and anchorages for the cables (B) under tensile stress.

horizontal components of the tension in the two stays can be taken care of, leaving only a vertical pull to be borne by the cable anchorages. An interesting example of this form of suspension design is the Mariakerke bridge near Ghent in Belgium. Bridges of this type are practical up to about 300 m. span.

The second variation is to be found in San Francisco's remarkable Bay bridge, which includes two 700-m. suspension spans end to end. Here the two pairs of stays on the adjoining ends of the suspension spans are fixed to a common anchorage. The horizontal components of the tensions in these cables are equal and opposite so far as the dead weight is concerned and so cancel each other out. The common pier is therefore primarily a gravity anchorage holding the combined vertical pull from the two pairs of stays. However it also has to withstand the resultant of the horizontal components of the additional stay tensions caused by traffic crossing the bridge.

A technique sometimes used in modern suspension bridges is prestressing of the main cables, hangers, and deck by jacking up the towers, which are independent of the deck, after construction is complete. The towers of the Mariakerke bridge were raised 35 cm. after the deck had been completed. In Russia a new prestressing technique involves sloping instead of vertical towers, the angle resulting in forces that prestress the bridge.

Composite Bridges   Many bridges are of composite design. Canti-

The Mariakerke suspension bridge, Belgium. By incorporating a long strut between the ends of the stays, the opposing horizontal components of the tension in the two stays can be taken care of, leaving only a vertical pull to be sustained by the cable anchorages.

lever bridges are usually, though not always, designed with a gap between two cantilever arms, this gap being bridged by a simple beam, usually a truss. Many large arch and cantilever spans have approaches made up of a series of comparatively short beams. The 12.4-km. Hampton Roads bridge complex near the mouth of Chesapeake Bay on the east US coast includes three cantilevers, a suspension span, a truss, and a series of simple beams.

A fairly recent design innovation is the "bridle chord" bridge. This consists of a long beam, which may be a contilever, partly supported by cables from one or more towers; it may be thought of as a combination of a beam and a suspension bridge. In some situations it is cheaper than either.

A multiple bridge designed in the space-age idiom is the six-span St. Michel "portal" bridge at Toulouse, France. This bridge is, in fact, a series of identical hinged portal arches, the intervening gaps being bridged by short cantilevers.

Movable Bridges Though all movable bridges are variations of the three basic types, they form a family of their own. The need for such bridges arises where substantial headroom is required for cross traffic below (as in a ship canal) but when a high-level fixed bridge would be uneconomical. Movable bridges are usually either swing, bascule, or lift.

Swing bridges have the disadvantage that the opening they provide is necessarily less than half their length, since they pivot about a central point. The world's longest, the Mississippi swing railroad bridge at Fort Madison, USA, completed in 1927, is 158 m. long, but when open, provides a maximum navigation channel hardly 75 m. wide.

London's historic Tower bridge is the classic example of the *bascule*. Here there are two counterweighted cantilevers supported on horizontal pivots. When traffic is to pass below, the "leaves" are raised. A more modern example is the 100-m. bascule at Sault Ste. Marie, Michigan, USA; it holds the span record for this class of bridge, and was built in 1941.

The *vertical lift* bridge usually consists of a beam end-supported from towers by vertical cables, like a huge horizontal elevator. The world's longest movable span is one of these, the 167-m. Arthur Kill railway bridge at Elizabeth, New Jersey, USA, opened in 1959 and illustrated on page 87.

At Basra there is a "sinking" bridge across the Shatt al Arab. The brainchild of an Indian army engineer who, during World War II, could not get the materials he required for a more conventional lift bridge, the main span is lowered until it is about 7 m. under water, deep enough for river traffic to pass over it.

Once a decision has been taken on the type of bridge that will best suit the situation (there may be more than one feasible

Two examples of composite bridges. North bridge, Dusseldorf (top), is a bridle-chord bridge, which is a long beam partly supported by cables from one or more towers. Below: the six-span St. Michel portal bridge at Toulouse, France, is a series of identical three-hinged arches (that is, pinmounted at both ends and crown), intervening gaps being bridged by short cantilevers.

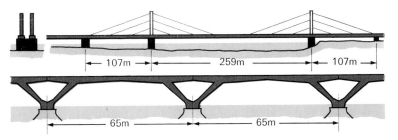

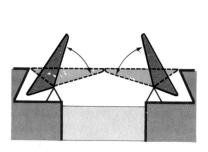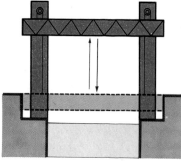

Two kinds of movable bridge. In the bascule bridge (left) two counterweight cantilevers supported on horizontal pivots can be raised when traffic is to pass below. London's Tower bridge is an example of this type. The vertical lift bridge (right) usually consists of a beam end-supported from towers by vertical cables, like a huge horizontal elevator. Opposite: the Arthur Kill railroad vertical lift bridge, New Jersey, U.S.A., is the world's largest.

alternative, the choice being finally dictated, perhaps, by the aesthetic appearance of a particular proposal, or by a first estimate of cost) the engineer has to attend to the specification of materials. What, precisely, will the bridge and its foundations be made of?

Materials

Queen Semiramis of Babylon commanded the building of a bridge across the Euphrates in about 2100 B.C. We are told that the river was diverted while the foundations were built, that the latter were made of stone blocks anchored together with iron bars grouted into holes with molten lead, and that the 10-m.-wide carriageway was made of cedar and cypress.

The wooden bridges of early civilizations were replaced gradually, during the next 2000 years, by stone arches, of which the Etruscans, the Mexicans, the Chinese, and the Persians left many fine examples even before the Romans built their imposing bridges. The first iron bridge on record was a 33-m. cast-iron arch across the River Severn at Coalbrookdale, England, completed in 1779. Fifty years later wrought iron had been developed. A 200-m. chain link suspension bridge (opened in 1849) across the Danube at Budapest, Hungary, was a fine early example of how engineers exploited this new material by forming it into either link or "eyebar" chains.

I have described in Chapter 1 how Bessemer's process for the manufacture of steel was first announced in 1856. It was inevitable that steel should soon become widely specified for bridges, though in Britain a conservative Board of Trade (recently stunned by the Tay bridge disaster described on page 97) prohibited its use in bridges until the Siemens open-hearth process had been developed some years later. The first great triumph of steel in bridge construction was seen in James Eads's massive St. Louis railroad bridge across the Mississippi, completed in 1873. It had three steel arches, one of 156 m. span, two of 150 m.

Today the bridge designer has a wide range of structural steels from which to choose, a variety of prefabricated rolled shapes and sections he can use, new economical methods of shaping, cutting, and jointing—all factors that can reduce cost and that undoubtedly influence design. The introduction of welding alone, by replacing rivets, made possible a 20 per cent saving in steel for a typical jointed structure of a given strength. Welding also makes for simpler detail and easier maintenance.

Here I shall mention only one particular form of high-tensile steel of unique importance to the bridge designer. This is the 0.49-cm.-diameter cold-drawn galvanized-steel wire, commonly used for the cables of long-span suspension bridges. The precise dimension I have mentioned may sound puzzling. Experience has shown that this wire, which can be manufactured with an ultimate strength approaching 17250 kg/cm², is both the thinnest and thickest that suits the particular application. Thinner wire can be made stronger, but cable spinning would take much longer and cost disproportionately more. Nor would thicker wire make spinning cheaper, as it would be too stiff to run through the sheaves in the cable-spinning process described in Chapter 5. So 0.49-cm.-diameter wire has become the standard for cables spun on site.

Cables made up of parallel wires are not universal. Some suspension bridges have their cables built up of coiled steel-wire ropes. The 610-m. Tancarville suspension bridge over the Seine, above Le Havre, France, completed in 1959, is a recent example; it has two main cables, each made up of 60 twisted steel-wire ropes.

Since World War II there has been a trend toward using "battledeck" construction for the roadway of long-span bridges. This, as its name implies, is a form of construction developed for the decks of fighting ships. It consists of several steel plates welded together, with stiffening sections welded on below, the whole supported on conventional *stringers* (longitudinal members) and cross girders. For its weight a battledeck is considerably stronger than a reinforced concrete slab, and on long spans, where excessive dead weight is an expensive luxury, the use of the battledeck with a thin wearing surface of, say, tarmac can result in savings.

The use of steel is almost universal in modern bridging. Because it withstands tension as well as thrust it is ideal for the box girders and trusses of large beam and cantilever bridges. For the same reason it is used to build the towers of large suspension bridges; these towers have not only to withstand the great weight of the cables, roadway, and stiffening trusses (a downward compressive force), but must be stiff enough to bear immense bending stresses (which include tension) caused by lateral wind pressure. Even where concrete is the basic material of a bridge, steel is used to reinforce it.

When designing in steel the engineer must take steps against corrosion. Current practice is to clean the steel before erection by blasting with metal grit; then to spray it with a coat of non-corrosive metal, usually zinc or aluminum, from 0.005 to 0.015 cm. thick; finally to apply several coats of weather-resistant paint.

Even after this treatment every part of a steel construction should be accessible for inspection and maintenance painting. The towers of the Verrazano-Narrows suspension bridge are built up of vertical cells, each 105 cm. square. There are 92 of these cells at the base of the tower, and every cell is accessible.

This constant fight against corrosion is so expensive that the prudent engineer keenly watches the development of new grades of structural stainless steel. Already such steel is made with the qualities the engineer requires. As soon as production becomes less costly he will make full use of this important new material.

In Chapter 1 I mentioned new aluminum alloys that are as strong as some steels, yet less than half the weight. They are also noncorrosive, and require no protection from the elements. Though these alloys are priced five to six times higher than comparable steels, there are already some all-aluminum bridges in existence, notable among them being the 87-m. Arvida bridge, an unpainted aluminum arch spanning the Saguenay River in Canada. This weighs 193,000 kg., very much lighter than the 437,000 kg. at which a comparable steel arch would have turned the scales. Here it was decided that the considerable recurring saving in maintenance costs and the saving on the foundations (due to the arch being so much lighter) justified the substantially higher capital cost of the aluminum.

Describing the technology of concrete in Chapter 1, I explained how concrete can be laid under water—even salt water—which is sometimes useful during the building of bridge foundations. Entrenched as it is in many areas of civil engineering, concrete in its various forms is one of the contemporary bridge designer's most versatile materials.

In Germany, where post-World War II reconstruction provided engineers with a unique opportunity to display skill and originality in the field of bridge design, it has been found that for general road bridges of under 200 m. span the steel box girder is usually most economical. But prestressed concrete, which is growing cheaper as its technology matures, is already a vigorous competitor as a material for beam bridges up to 150 m. in length. A fine example, completed in 1963, is the prestressed-concrete cantilever of box design that carries Britain's M2 motorway over

The 76-m. Arvida bridge over the Saguenay River, Canada, is an arch made en tirely of unpainted non-corrosive aluminum. Savings on maintenance and on the foundations (aluminum being much lighter than alternative metals such as steel) justified the substantially higher capital cost of the aluminum.

the River Medway near Rochester. This challenge from concrete is not necessarily a worldwide phenomenon. Prestressed-concrete construction requires more highly qualified supervision than the erection of steel girders. Consequently in the USA, where technical skill and experience is more expensive than elsewhere, steel bridges in the under-150-m. area still have an economic edge over their prestressed-concrete cousins.

But even prefabricated prestressed-concrete lattice girders, which should not be so demanding in terms of erection skill, have lately been shown to be not only practical but economic. The first of this type was the Mangfall bridge (built in 1960), which carries the Munich-Salzburg autobahn over the Mangfall valley. It has a 106-m. central span and two 89-m. approach spans, supported on tall reinforced-concrete columns. A recent multispan continuous-beam bridge in prestressed concrete was completed in 1957 over the Moskva River in the USSR. It has a center span of 146 m. and anchor spans of 43 m.

The specification of prefabricated concrete components in

bridge design is a rapidly growing trend. Sometimes these parts are prestressed in the factory, sometimes they are stressed after assembly by threading the stressing cables or wires through channels left in the concrete. The five-span Narrows bridge, which crosses the Swan River at Perth, Australia (completed in 1959, longest span 96 m.), was assembled from precast units, longitudinal prestressing being accomplished by laying 1.75-cm.-diameter cables alongside the webs of the concrete sections, and then tensioning them. Prestressed-concrete pipes, too, are now widely used in bridge foundation work, as we shall see.

Foundations

The design of a bridge's foundations is as important a part of the exercise as the design of its load-bearing spans. The weight of structural steel in the Verrazano-Narrows suspension bridge—including the towers, the four main cables, the double-deck roadway, and the stiffening truss—is about 153 million kg. The two main foundations not only share this enormous load, but add to it their own great weight. The towers of this bridge are founded in shallow water about 100 meters from the shore, on concrete piers. These extend downward through mud, sand, and rock overburden to solid rock, which was found 32 m. below the surface on the Staten Island side, 51 m. down on the other. The design of these piers is simplicity itself; each is a 69 m. × 39 m. reinforced-concrete monolith. How piers of this kind are built will be explained in detail in Chapter 5.

The Verrazano-Narrows bridge foundations are typical of their kind, though, where extraneous pressures are expected, they are sometimes founded or keyed deep into the bedrock instead of just being laid, as it were, on its surface. The south pier of the Golden Gate suspension bridge, located in 20 m. of seawater, was designed to withstand the constant ebb and flow of the tide and the buffeting of Pacific waves in a potentially stormy situation. What is more, the bridge stands in an earthquake belt, and was designed to remain stable in the event of moderate tremors. This particular pier was designed to stand on a pedestal keyed 4.5 m. into submarine rock, the whole structure being raised within a substantial breakwater.

The main piers of the huge Mackinac suspension bridge, which crosses the Mississippi in an area subject to extremely severe winters, were designed to withstand a pack ice pressure of over 17,000 kg/m linear; they are not only keyed into bedrock over 30 m. below water level, but are provided with pedestals designed to present the minimum obstruction to drifting ice.

Where the load on a bridge pier is not too great, and where rock is at such a depth that it cannot be reached economically, a pile foundation is often specified by the designer. For example, the foundations of the 37-km. Pontchartrain Lake bridge, Louisiana, USA, consists of 23.5-m. prestressed hollow concrete tubes driven into the lake bed.

In the USSR prefabricated reinforced-concrete cylinders have been used for the foundations of many hundreds of bridges built over the Volga, the Don, the Dnieper, and other major rivers during the past 10 years. These cylinders vary from about 1.5 to 6 m. in diameter, and are from 7.5 to 8.75 cm. thick. Supplied to the bridge sites in standard lengths, these are joined together as required during the sinking process, using steel junction flanges. Where the engineer considers it necessary these cylinder piles are finally dredged out and packed with concrete. The huge Wuhan double-deck road and rail bridge over the Yangtze River in China (completed in 1957) is founded on groups of 1.5-m.-diameter reinforced-concrete piles keyed into bedrock 40 m. below water level and finally filled with more concrete.

Steel tubes, too, are used as piles for bridge foundations. An example is the Narrows bridge over the Swan River at Perth, Australia, where 54-m.-long, 80-cm.-diameter hollow steel piles, lengthened where necessary by welding on additional sections, were driven to bear a load of 254,000 kg. each, then filled with reinforced concrete.

When the bed of the Hudson River was surveyed for the foundations of the Tappan Zee bridge main navigation span it was found to be soft and yielding to a very great depth; a conventional foundation capable of supporting the heavy steel cantilevers would have proved very expensive. An ingenious alternative was devised. This was the provision, under each pier, of a huge (57 m. × 30 m. × 10 m.) hollow concrete box resting on a bed of piles. By making the boxes watertight and pumping them dry while the cantilevers were being erected, they became buoyant enough to support 70 per cent of the weight of the finished bridge, leaving only 30 per cent for the piles to carry. The Milovan bridge in Macedonia, built in 1935, used this same principle on a smaller scale.

A brilliantly audacious bridge foundation feature is to be found on the multispan bridge that carries the autobahn over the Ruhr River at Duisburg, opened in 1963. Soil experts knew that the ground in the vicinity of the river was liable to subsidence under load, due to old coal workings. Using the latest soil mechanics techniques, they estimated that a subsidence of up to 2 m. was to be expected during the first eight years of the bridge's life, after which the ground would be stable. To allow for this the pier designs included a system of hydraulic jacks and packing by which the spans are being maintained at their original level until the expected subsidence is complete. There are horizontal jacks, too, to correct any lateral settlement of the piers.

The abutments of arches, as we have seen, must bear huge angular thrusts. The four bearings of the Sydney Harbor bridge, for example, each withstand a pressure of 20 million kg. at 45° to the horizontal. To ensure stable foundations for this concentrated angular load the designer stipulated excavation of the surface rock to a depth of between 10 and 12 m. The 30 m. × 10 m. × 10 m. rock trenches that were cut were then filled with solid concrete, but to avoid horizontal planes between the lifts (which might have resulted in a tendency under sideways loading to horizontal shearing), laying of the concrete was done in the form of

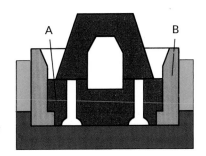

Cross section of the south pier of Golden Gate suspension bridge, San Francisco. Because of the danger of storms and earth tremors, this pier was designed to stand on a concrete foundation (A) keyed 5 m. into the submarine rock, the whole being raised within a substantial breakwater (B).

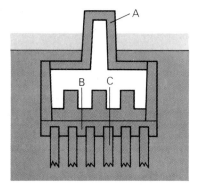

Cross section of a buoyant pier in the Milovan bridge, Central Macedonia. Here foundations had to be built on mud, and the strengthened hollow concrete box (A) provides buoyancy below mud level. It rests on a concrete raft (B) that in turn rests on concrete piles (C).

hexagonal cells. Most of the mass of these foundations is of standard concrete, but toward the corner where the 23.75-cm.-thick high-tensile bearing plates are located, two superior grades of concrete were used, the strongest directly under the steel. Moreover to ensure an equally distributed load through the foundation the maximum error permitted by the designer in the placing of the bearing plates was 0.0025 cm.

One foundation of the 301-m. Hell Gate steel arch bridge over the East River at New York presented unusual difficulty. Survey had shown that firm rock was located 20 m. below water level. But when the river bed was excavated to reach the rock a crevasse was found, varying from 5 to 20 m. in width and of unknown depth. To ensure a safe foundation the engineer in charge decided first to bridge the crevasse under water with a solid concrete arch, onto the crown of which the main abutment of the bridge was founded.

The three concrete arch bridges of the Caracas Autopista, described in Chapter 3, were founded in the sides of mountain ravines. The rock was too porous and brittle to bear the great thrust of the arches directly, and the problem was solved by letting huge concrete plugs into the mountainside. Holes were dug, 2 m. in diameter and 20 m. deep, with their ends enlarged like elephant's feet, and concrete was packed into these holes. The resulting plugs, with their enlarged feet bedded deep, provided simple but safe foundations.

The anchorages of a cantilever bridge present the designer with little difficulty. The upward thrust is never excessive, being partly balanced by the dead weight of the anchor arm. Not so the anchorages of large suspension bridges, which have to hold fast against the immense tension in the main cables. There are two basic ways of providing such anchorages, of equal importance. Where the bedrock is firm and sufficiently near the surface the supporting cradle for the cables can be anchored by means of a concrete plug let into a shaft cut in the rock. Where the rock is too weak or too deep the alternative is a gravity anchorage—a solid block of concrete that resists the tension in the cables by its immense weight alone.

A recent example of a gravity anchorage is to be found in the Verrazano-Narrows bridge. The western anchorage is a concrete monolith 66 m. wide, 96 m. long, founded 23 m. below ground level on compact glacial sand. The anchorage at the other end is somewhat larger, but is founded only 16 m. down. During the building of these two huge anchorages (one illustrated on page 133) they were provided with spread footings to prevent settlement due to their great weight, before attachment of the bridge cables.

We have seen that the Bay bridge, San Francisco, has a common anchorage at the junction of the two suspension spans. Here the designer was faced with deep seawater, a swift tide, and a sloping rock bed under the sea mud, 60 m. below water level. The anchorage was designed as a solid concrete block, 60 m. × 28 m. in plan, resting on the rock, which was suitably leveled, and extending to the high water mark. Above this is a hollow concrete pier that accommodates the frames to which the cables are anchored. The block is built up of vertical steel cylinders that were filled with concrete after being placed in position.

The designers of the new Forth suspension bridge, Scotland, were able to found their cable anchorages in hard rock located near the surface of the ground, and so settled for the plug. An inclined tunnel was made 60 m. into the rock for each anchorage. Into each tunnel was poured approximately 17 million kg. of concrete, a high-tensile-steel slab, designed for attaching the main cables, being mounted over the face of the plug. Each slab was tied back to the far end of its plug by means of 114 high-tensile prestressed-steel cables—the first time the technique of prestressing had been used in such an anchorage. By prestressing these cables to a tension greater than that in the main bridge cables, subsequent stretching that would have weakened the plugs was avoided. If prestressing had not been used the plugs would have had to have been much larger with considerably more steel reinforcement, and therefore more costly.

Research

Research has become almost a disease. Millions are spent on finding the answers to questions, often simple, which the world has formerly been content to leave unprobed. The justification comes in many forms—added safety, added efficiency, reduction in costs. It is the engineer who is destined to apply most of the findings of current research in his everyday work, not least the civil engineer. It is research into the properties of steel, above all, that has made possible some of the magnificent recent bridges.

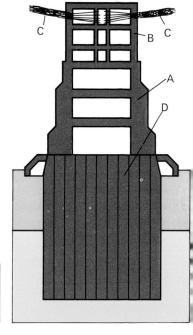

Right: cross section of central anchorage of the San Francisco double suspension bridge, showing how the hollow concrete pier (A) accommodating the frames (B) to which the cables (C) are anchored, is built on a block of vertical steel cylinders (D) filled with concrete. Below: cross section of an abutment of Sydney Harbor bridge; each of these has to withstand 20 million kg. Diagram shows use of standard good-quality concrete (A), medium strength concrete (B), maximum strength concrete (C), and steel bearing plate (D).

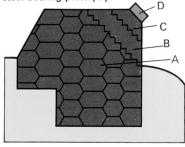

Research into the materials and processes of bridge construction is one thing; research on the quality, strength, and efficiency of the finished product quite another. For bridges are often so huge and costly that there is no question of building prototypes for testing. Each great bridge is a custom-built one-off job. It must fulfil its purpose completely, or its designer may lose a reputation, even ruin a career, as the world's first major bridge disaster proved. This was the collapse of the undistinguished 3.2-km. Tay bridge in Scotland (completed 1878), in the center of which were thirteen 74-m. wrought-iron trusses on tall cast-iron columns rising from brick and concrete piers. Designed by Sir Thomas Bouch, a British railroad engineer of repute, it carried rail traffic across the river for 19 uneventful months. Then one stormy December night a complete passenger train disappeared, literally, while crossing the bridge. All 13 main spans came down and there were no survivors.

To this day no one knows the exact cause of the disaster, though various theories have been advanced. The most plausible is that a sudden gust of wind, blowing broadside on to the train as it crossed the bridge, resulted in a sideways thrust the bridge could not withstand. Whatever the cause Sir Thomas Bouch was forced to admit that adequate provision for wind pressure had not been made; he lost both his reputation and a commission to design a railroad bridge over the Firth of Forth, and died within a year, apparently of a broken heart. When a new Tay bridge was opened nine years later its design allowed for a lateral wind pressure of 275 kg/cm², a figure considerably higher than that generally accepted today, as a result of formal research, for bridges in a similar situation.

The Tay bridge disaster was due, it is presumed, to aerostatic instability—quite a different ailment from that which caused the failure of a number of early suspension bridges; their weakness was a lack of aerodynamic rigidity.

The most notable of the suspension bridge failures was the collapse in a gale of the first Tacoma Narrows bridge in 1940, only four months after it had been opened. Though this bridge was unusually narrow (12 m.) for its length (840 m.), and had plate girders only 3 m. deep for longitudinal stiffening, it was correctly

Dramatic shots from the film taken of the Tacoma Narrows suspension bridge during the hours leading up to its collapse in a gale in 1940, only four months after it was opened. All subsequent aerodynamic research is based upon this visual record of the vibrations to which the bridge was prone during winds of known force and direction. Today aerodynamic research is an essential to the design phase of every major suspension bridge.

designed according to engineering knowledge and practice of the time. That a 65 km/h gale was able to induce 10-m.-high "waves" along the roadway of the bridge, as well as serious lateral swaying, so shocked the engineering world that extensive aerodynamic research is today an essential part of the design phase of every major suspension bridge.

It is of interest here to see how the Tacoma bridge disaster not only brought home the need for such research, but provided invaluable material on which it has been possible to base all subsequent research. It so happened that a cine film had been made of the Tacoma bridge, during the gale, at the time of its collapse, providing a detailed and accurate permanent visual record of the vibrations to which it was prone in winds of known force and direction. Engineers at the University of Washington, after studying this film, built a 1:50 scale model of the bridge and the University provided a 30-m. wind tunnel in which to test the model. After experiments to establish the effect of scale on the many variables involved, the researchers were able successfully to reproduce the oscillations recorded in the film on the model in the wind tunnel. Also, more important, they were able to establish the data necessary to ensure accurate prediction, by wind-tunnel testing of models, of the behavior of projected new bridges under known conditions.

Sir Gilbert Roberts, responsible for most of the technical innovations on the remarkable 972-m. suspension bridge, opened in September 1966, which crosses the River Severn between England and Wales, had a series of 1:100 scale models of the proposed bridge, involving major variations in design, repeatedly tested in a 20-m. wind tunnel at Britain's National Physical Laboratory, before the final revolutionary weight- and money-saving design emerged. In this wind tunnel the bridge was mounted on a turntable that provided not only a 90° horizontal rotation, but a tilting action along the axis of the bridge so that nonhorizontal winds could be simulated. When the basic design had been decided additional tests were made on portions of the bridge modeled to a scale of 1:32.

The 972-m. Severn bridge, in its final form, underlines two entirely new directions now evident in suspension bridge design. They concern the towers and the road deck.

The tower heights of all the great suspension bridges have remained remarkably uniform, varying by no more than is accountable for by differences in span and in the height of the roadway above water level. A comparison of their weights, however, discloses a very different picture. The towers of the George Washington bridge each weighed nearly 21 million kg., of the Golden Gate bridge 22 million kg., and of the Verrazano-Narrows bridge 28 million kg. Yet the towers of the Severn bridge weigh a puny 2 million kg. Recent American suspension bridges have all had steel towers of the now traditional cellular design (as we have seen, those of the Verrazano-Narrows bridge, at their base, are each made up of 92 cells 105 m. square). But the Severn bridge towers are each built of four stiffened welded steel

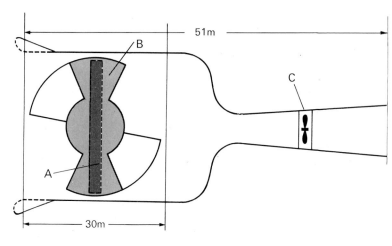

Plan of the wind tunnel used to test scale models of the Severn suspension bridge. A 1:100 scale model of the bridge (A) was mounted on a turntable (B) providing not only 90° horizontal rotation but also a tilting action along the bridge's axis so that nonhorizontal winds could be simulated by means of a tunnel fan (C).

plates, friction-bolted together, with the steel concentrated exactly where it is most wanted to withstand the anticipated bending stresses. Tests have shown this new lightweight construction to be as rigid as the old, and the cost saving is sensational.

The second innovation in the Severn bridge is to be found in the design of its deck. All the older bridges had a conventional flat deck stiffened longitudinally and laterally by girders, usually of truss design. Described as a "torsion box," the Severn bridge deck is more like a continuous aerofoil. Proved in the wind tunnel to provide more stability than a far larger conventional truss design, this streamlined torsion box is cheaper. Combined with hangers fitted diagonally instead of vertically (as is usual) this deck design makes for a more stable bridge at considerably less cost. Time will tell how effective these new design concepts are in practice. If the wind tunnel findings are correct the Severn bridge will surely set a new fashion.

Wind tunnel testing is not confined to suspension bridges. The Birchenough bridge in Rhodesia—an extremely light, long steel

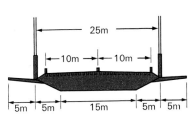

Above: simplified cross section of the hollow streamlined torsion box deck of the recently opened Severn suspension bridge. It resembles a continuous aerofoil and is cheaper and more stable than the conventional flat deck, which is stiffened longitudinally and laterally by means of truss girders.

Right: a section of this torsion box deck being hoisted into position.

arch, completed in 1935—was tested for stability during erection, using a scale model in a wind tunnel. In fact this was probably the earliest use of this technique in bridge design. Scale models of bridges have been used in other departments of research. An interesting case occurred in the design stage of the three arch bridges on the Caracas Autopista in Venezuela. As I shall be describing the unusual construction process used in these bridges in Chapter 5, I will discuss these model tests in the same chapter when their precise purpose will be more easily appreciated.

Loading tests are sometimes carried out on completed bridges to check whether the actual deflection under load corresponds with the calculated figure. One method is to use an especially built loading vehicle that is moved onto the bridge while continuous deflection and strain-gauge readings are taken. The British Ministry of Transport has a 100,000-kg. vehicle running on two bogies, each having two axles carrying four solid 37.5-cm. tires. The loading on either bogie can be varied from 20,000 to 90,000 kg., the other carrying the balance of the total weight.

Loading a complete bridge to destruction, as a research study, is obviously rarely possible. But an opportunity for such a test arose when the decision was taken to demolish a comparatively new 85-m. prestressed-concrete bridge as part of the site preparation for the 1951 Festival of Britain. This bridge had been prestressed on the Freyssinet principle, using 24 twelve-wire cables tensioned to 30,000 kg. The concrete had a crushing strength (tested 28 days after pouring) of 31,000 kg/m². The design load of the bridge was 490 kg/m². This load was first placed on the bridge, the deflection being noted: The bridge was then loaded to 600 kg/m² and to 735 kg/m², the increased deflections also being measured. The latter load was left on the bridge overnight, after which it was removed and the recovery measured. Up to this point the structure had withstood a sustained overload of 50 per cent without damage. The bridge was next reloaded with a 100 per cent overload. The deflection was noted and crack formation recorded. The load was again removed and recovery measured. On the third day of testing the bridge was loaded to failure. This occurred when the equivalent of 50 kg/cm² was added to the 5800 kg/cm² already on the bridge. The full test, which showed the bridge capable of safely withstanding an overload in excess of 100 per cent, disclosed that there had in fact been no general failure of the steel cables. The cause of final collapse was apparently failure of the bond between the steel and the concrete.

An electronic computer was used extensively during the design of the recently completed Tancarville suspension bridge across the Seine above Le Havre. It helped the engineers to solve various problems in a fraction of the time that human calculation would have taken; one such was the extremely complex task of predicting the extent of distortion that would occur during erection and the resulting additional stressing of the various parts of the bridge.

The use of the computer in bridge design is a comparatively recent development, but one that is destined to become standard practice for all large-scale work. The calculation of the stresses and strains in the various parts of a large modern bridge is a tedious and time-consuming operation, yet the ultimate safety of every human being who crosses the bridge may depend on the accuracy and thoroughness of those calculations. An engineer trained in the programing of a computer for complex stress analysis can obtain from the device, in the time it takes to feed in the problems and read the results, the answers to calculations that would otherwise take an army of trained men months to work out. He can equally easily obtain what the mathematician can only estimate after a laborious series of calculations—continuous curves that immediately disclose the stress peaks in the various bridge members under a comprehensive range of conditions, covering all possible combinations of moving live loads, varying wind pressures from various directions, and any other variables that may be involved. When computers are programed to *design* new bridges (as opposed to merely calculate for the human designer), who knows what may emerge?

5 The Construction of Bridges

Before we move on to see how great bridges are built, how their foundations are often made to penetrate through the bed of rivers, down to rock, a brief review of some of the world's greatest bridges should prove instructive; it will also fill in some of the more glaring gaps in the picture the reader may still have in his mind after reading Chapter 4.

As we have seen, high-tensile steel wire has the highest strength/weight ratio of all the materials available to the civil engineer. It is logical, therefore, to find suspension bridges, which make use of such wire to support the roadway, high in any record of bridging achievement. In fact there are 15 suspension bridges in service today that span a greater distance than the longest of all other types of bridge, and more are being built. But in reviewing the world's great bridging achievements it is not only the span we should measure and consider. A bridge's strength is often as important as its span, sometimes more so. Nor should achievement be reckoned only in terms of absolute dimensions.

Nearly 30,000 km. of pencil-thin steel wire were spun together to make the four main cables of the Verrazano-Narrows suspension bridge, New York. The method used is described on page 106. Here one of the completed cables is being compacted hydraulically and bound into cylindrical shape.

The longest concrete or steel arches are as much feats of engineering as are the long suspension bridges. So are some shorter bridges of new and unusual design.

The World "Top Ten" Bridges

Listed below are what may perhaps be called the "top ten" among the world's great bridges. The list includes bridges of various merits; and though it may not be final and can never be complete, it gives an illuminating glimpse of the total achievement in the sphere of bridge construction in the year 1967.

1. Verrazano-Narrows bridge, New York. Longest span. This great new American suspension bridge, designed by O. H. Ammann (who, as we shall see, is represented three times in this short list), stands at the entrance to New York Harbor and was completed in 1964. Of conventional design (photograph on page 104), its main span is a majestic 1280 m., 65 m. above the water, its total length including approaches adding to 4 km. This mighty bridge is designed to carry 12 automobile lanes on two decks, and cost around $325 million. Its towers, each weighing 27 million kg., are 204 m. high. Its four 90-cm.-diameter cables are each made up of 26,106 galvanized cold-drawn 0.49-cm. steel wires—a total of 228,000 km. of wire, enough to wind five times around the earth at the equator.

2. George Washington bridge, New York. Strongest suspension bridge. One of the most remarkable features of this 35-year-old bridge (an early design of O. H. Ammann) is its great traffic capacity. Built at a time when six automobile lanes was considered a generous concession to future development, this bridge today has 14, more than any other long-span bridge. Originally the bridge was intended to carry four tramway lines below the original roadway; but though these were never installed, the four cables designed to give it the necessary strength were fortunately retained, making possible the bridge's second road deck in 1962. When first opened, and for six years, this bridge had the world's longest span; it ranks fourth today after the Verrazano-Narrows, the Golden Gate, and the Mackinac bridges. The four original 90-cm.-diameter cables are each made of 26,474 galvanized steel wires, 0.49 cm. diameter, running to a total length of 168,000 km.

and give the bridge a live load strength of 7560 kg. per meter run (the Verrazano bridge's comparable statistic being 6580). The George Washington bridge's towers rise 179 m. high, each weighing 21 million kg. The cost in 1931 was $75 million, the second deck and its approach roads adding (at 1962 prices) $173 million to the original sum. Economists can adjust and compare these figures.

3. Quebec bridge, Canada. Longest cantilever span. Before the development of high-tensile steel wire suitable for suspension bridge cables, cantilever bridges held the world record in span. They were strong stiff bridges of great load-carrying capacity. The Quebec bridge, completed in 1918, bridges a gap of 540 m. between the two main piers, carries two mainline railroad tracks, and achieved a live load strength of 15,000 kg. per meter run. Designed by Theodore Cooper, it was for 11 years the world's longest span bridge of any type, the Ambassador suspension bridge at Detroit exceeding its span by 15 m. in 1929.

4. Bayonne bridge, New York. Longest steel arch. This fine bridge, another of O. H. Ammann's designs, crosses the Kill Van Kull strait at New York. With its span of 496 m. it is just one meter longer than the Sydney Harbor bridge, completed one year later. The Bayonne bridge carries two urban rail lines, six automobile lanes, and has a live load strength of 9500 kg. per meter run.

5. Sydney Harbor bridge, Australia. Strongest long arch. But for the Bayonne bridge's extra meter, this 495-m. steel arch, designed by Sir Ralph Freeman, would qualify for fourth place in the "top ten." It is considerably stronger than the Bayonne bridge (16,200 kg. live load per meter run), carries four urban rail lines and six automobile lanes, and passes a majestic 52 m. above the water. Unlike the Bayonne bridge, which was built with the aid of temporary trestle falsework, the Sydney Harbor bridge crosses deep tidal water, and was constructed by the cantilever method (described on page 124), a formidable problem with a 39-million-kg. arch. It is the world's second strongest long-span bridge.

6. Gladesville bridge, Sydney, Australia. Longest concrete arch. This elegant eight-auto-lane bridge over the Parramatta River, the western branch of Sydney Harbor, has a main span of 305 m., is the world's largest concrete bridge, and was completed in 1964

*New York's fine Bayonne bridge is the longest steel arch in the world.
Designed by O. H. Ammann and built with the aid of temporary trestle
falsework, it has a 496-m. span and carries two urban rail lines and six
automobile lanes.*

at a cost of £A2.4 million. Designed by a firm of consulting engineers, G. A. Mansell & Partners, it is followed closely in span, for bridges of its type, by the 285-m. Foz do Iguaçú, on the Brazil-Paraguay border and the 266-m. Arrábida bridge in Portugal (both completed in 1963). A photograph of the Gladesville bridge taken during construction appears on page 128.

7. Hell Gate bridge, New York. Strongest steel arch. This 303-m. bridge is remarkable for its age. Completed in 1916 to a design by Gustav Lindenthal, it was for 16 years the longest arch span in the world and, though it now ranks fifth in its class for span, it is still today by far the most heavily loaded long-span bridge. It carries four mainline railroad tracks, and is capable of bearing a live load of 32,400 kg. per meter run.

Above: Britain's 150-m.-span Medway bridge, opened in 1966, is among the finest examples of the use of prestressed concrete where formerly steel alone would have been used. An interesting feature is the unusual length of the anchor arms, each of which is 94 m., more than half the length of the entire main span. Below: Sydney's Gladesville bridge, completed in 1964, is the world's largest concrete bridge with a main span of 305 m. The four ribs of the arch were built of precast box units on movable falsework as illustrated on page 128.

8. Severin bridge, Cologne. Longest "bridle chord" box girder.
Opened in 1959, this is the longest of a postwar breed of bridges
in Europe where it was found that a box girder partly supported
by cables passing over a tower proved cheaper than either a plain
box girder or a suspension bridge in the 200–300-m. range. The
Severin bridge spans 297 m., is assymetrical, and has three sets
of cables, in pairs.
9. Sava bridge, Belgrade. Longest simple box girder. This 257-m.
bridge over the Sava River at Belgrade was completed in 1957 and
is notable as the longest self-supporting girder span in the world.
10. Medway bridge, Great Britain. Longest concrete cantilever.
A 150-m. span would hardly appear to deserve inclusion in a "top
ten" list, but this bridge is the finest example of the use of prestressed concrete where formerly only steel would have sufficed.
Illustrated on page 109, it consists of two cantilever arms, each
60 m. long, linked by a 30-m. suspended span—all of box girder
design in prestressed concrete. An interesting feature is the unusual length of the anchor arms; each is 94 m., more than half
the entire main span. The bridge's full length, excluding approaches, is 337 m., spanned in three great leaps.

In selecting the "top ten" I have had to ignore many other great
bridges; mention has already been made of some of these in the
previous chapter and details of others will be found in the pages
that follow. But before describing how these great bridges are
built I must mention four others that, though not in the "top
ten" today, are particularly noteworthy. Two of these each held

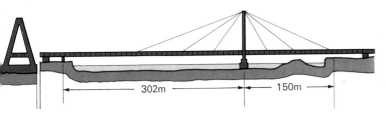

| 302m | 150m |

Opposite: New York's Hell Gate bridge, completed in 1916, is still the world's strongest steel arch. Above: section and side elevation of the Severin bridge, Cologne, a box girder partly supported by cables passing over a tower; this provides a cheaper solution for spans between about 200 and 350 m. than either a plain box girder or a suspension bridge.

the long-span record for more than a quarter of a century; the other two broke records for the economy achieved in their design and construction.

Forth rail bridge, Scotland. Greatest 19th-century bridge. Completed in 1890, this remarkable bridge, designed by Sir John Fowler and Sir Benjamin Baker, held the span record (513 m.) for 28 years, until the Quebec bridge appropriated the honor, but with only one long span against the Forth bridge's two. The bridge carries two mainline railroad tracks a clear 45 m. above the waters of the Firth of Forth, and was an unparalleled achievement for its day. Today it still ranks as one of the world's greatest bridges.

Golden Gate bridge, San Francisco. Pioneer long-span suspension bridge. Opened in 1937, this 1260-m. span was 210 m. more than the George Washington's and it only moved to second place among the world's mighty bridges when the Verrazano-Narrows bridge topped it by a humble 20 m. in 1964. With towers 224 m. high, each weighing 29 million kg., the bridge has two 90-cm.-diameter cables, carries six automobile lanes, bears a live load of 5400 kg. per meter run. Its south tower is founded 337 m. from the shore in 20 m. of tide-swept seawater.

Birchenough bridge, Rhodesia. Most economical long-span steel arch. This 324-m. high-tensile steel parabolic arch bridge, designed by Sir Ralph Freeman and completed in 1935, is a model of economical design, cost only $400,000 (1935 prices), and was the first long arch built for less than the cost of a comparable multi-

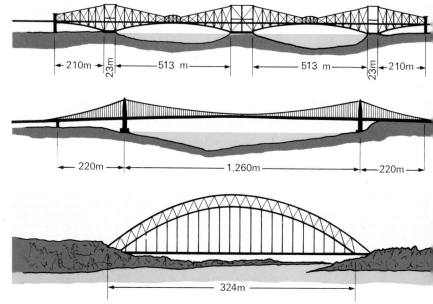

Top: Supreme among 19th-century bridges, the 513-m. Forth rail bridge in Scotland is a unique achievement for its day and age. Center: San Francisco's Golden Gate suspension bridge with its 1260-m. central span held the world record until the Verrazano-Narrows bridge topped it by a mere 20 m. in 1964. Bottom: the Birchenough 324-m. high-tensile parabolic steel arch bridge in Rhodesia is the world's most economic long-span steel arch.

span bridge. Carrying two lanes of automobile traffic, the bridge weighs a puny 3,150,000 kg. compared with the 59 million kg. of the Sydney Harbor bridge. Just one meter shorter than the Mersey River bridge at Widnes (upstream from Liverpool), England (1961), the Birchenough bridge holds fourth place among the world's long-span steel arches, and is 11 m. longer than the Sakai bridge, Nagasaki, Japan (1955), which is followed by New York's Hell Gate bridge.

Severn bridge, Great Britain. Most economical giant suspension bridge. Spanning 972 m., this recent (1966) suspension bridge is of highly economical design, carries four automobile lanes, and has a live load capacity of 1620 kg. per meter run; yet its own average dead weight per meter run is only 4050 kg., compared with the

Verrazano-Narrows bridge's 50,000 kg. The Severn bridge's 120-m. towers each weigh 1 million kg., compared with the Verrazano-Narrows bridge's 27-million-kg. towers. The cost of the Severn bridge was about $33 million, roughly one tenth of that of its big New York brother. The Severn bridge is illustrated on page 76.

So much for the vital statistics of the world's most important bridges; now let us take a closer look at the ways in which they were constructed.

Bridge Foundations

Bridge piers on dry land normally present no problem. Ground survey and design follow conventional principles. The method is that of excavation, preferably to bedrock, followed by the pouring of concrete, reinforced as required by design considerations. Sometimes, where bedrock is too deep, pile foundations may be specified. Here too their placing is carried out by the usual methods. Sometimes, on soft ground, a concrete pier foundation is built on the surface on a cutting edge and sunk into the soil or sand by excavating through open vertical shafts in the concrete block, thus undercutting its base so that it sinks into the ground under its own huge weight, guided by its sharp lower edges.

The foundations of the 450-m. Howrah cantilever bridge at Calcutta, India, were sunk in this manner. The two main pier foundations were each 54 m. × 24 m. divided into 21 vertical shafts, each 6 m. square with 2-m. walls between, through which the muck was excavated by mechanical grab. As the foundations sank, concrete was added to their walls to keep them above ground level. The north pier was finally founded in impervious clay 26 m. below ground; the shafts, pumped dry and cleaned, were then filled with concrete. On the south (Calcutta) side the pier base sank 31 m. before it settled on blue clay. As this was not watertight the subsoil water was excluded from the shafts, one by one, by sealing them with a vaulted steel roof and pumping in compressed air at a pressure of about 2.8 kg/cm^2. Men entered each pressurized chamber to clean it and fill it with concrete passed down through another air lock. Before this final concreting, the south pier, with its open shafts, was estimated to weigh about

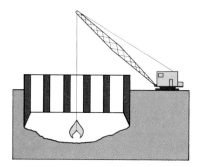

Sinking a concrete pier foundation by means of interior excavation. An excavator grab works between the vertical shafts of the concrete block whose sharp cutting edges sink into the ground under the pressure of its own weight.

11 million kg. The smaller anchorage piers of this bridge were sunk by the same method. At the bottom of each a horizontal steel grid was fitted, vertical steel anchor stays being attached to this grid before the spaces were filled up with concrete. The stays were subsequently attached to the anchor spans of the bridge.

Bridge piers are often founded under water—sometimes deep water—and here construction poses special problems. There are five accepted techniques:
1. Diversion of the water into a new channel;
2. Isolation of the pier sites by cofferdam;
3. Use of the pneumatic caisson;
4. Underwater excavation and concreting;
5. Driving piles through the water.

Diversion of the water implies that it is running; obviously this is economic only where the topography is suited to the method. To divert a river, even at an S bend, involves the building of a temporary dam and a temporary canal. Though used in the construction of permanent dams, this method is usually too costly for consideration at a bridge site.

A cofferdam is a wall driven into the water bed to isolate the area where work is to be undertaken. The water is pumped out of the enclosed space until the bed is dry enough for normal excavation and concreting. Such a wall is usually made of interlocking steel-sheet piling. The system works well where the water bed is not too hard for the piling to be driven and not so soft that water seepage from below exceeds the capacity of the pumps. In deep water it may be necessary to make a double-sheet pile wall, filling the gap with clay or concrete in order to achieve a watertight shell that will withstand the water pressure when the cofferdam has been pumped dry.

The piers of the Verrazano-Narrows bridge were sunk in the manner of the Howrah bridge; but as they stand in shallow water, rectangular cofferdams made of sheet pile cells were first placed and pumped dry. The cutting edge of each 70 m. × 40 m. main foundation was next assembled on the harbor bed. Finally a concrete slab was poured over it; in this were 66 circular 5-m.-diameter openings through which the grabs could work. One slab formed the base of each pier foundation, which was built up as it sank under its weight into the harbor bed.

The east pier of the recently completed Severn suspension bridge is founded in tidal water, and was built as a cofferdam that subsequently became the permanent wall of the pier. Men first worked in the water for 20-minute periods at each low tide, building the cofferdam in the form of a ring of concrete blocks. Once this wall had risen above high-water level it was pumped dry, the area inside being cleaned out down to bedrock, which was close to the river bed. Using steel wire ropes to anchor it to the rock and prestress it, the foundation was then completed by filling the cofferdam with concrete.

Sometimes the water bed is too soft for sheet piling to form a watertight wall, too hard for piles to penetrate, or too deep for any type of wall to be stable. It was for such situations that the pneumatic caisson was invented. First used by French engineers in the early years of the 19th century, a caisson is an enormous steel or concrete vessel (originally made of wood, bound with iron bands) with a lower cutting edge and an internal deck forming an airtight seal, sufficient depth being left below the deck for men to work on the water bed under it. The caisson is sunk at the site of the proposed pier, its sharp lower edge cutting into the

Section of a double-walled cofferdam. The gap between the two walls of steel sheet piles (A) is filled with clay or concrete in order to withstand the pressure of surrounding water when the working bed (B) is pumped dry.

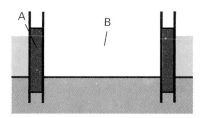

water bed. Compressed air is then pumped below the deck, excluding the water so that men can enter the pressurized chamber through air locks and work there. A separate air lock is provided through which excavated muck can be hauled out and concrete later lowered in.

The pneumatic caisson must be used with great caution. The air pressure must be carefully controlled; if it is too low, water will begin to flow in from below; if excessive, there is the danger of a "blow" in soft soil, the water being forced so far below the caisson's cutting edge that a huge bubble of compressed air escapes with a roar, mud and silt rushing in as the pressure is suddenly lowered.

Although men can work efficiently under considerable pressure, they must be gradually decompressed on emerging from the pressurized chamber; otherwise they may suffer *caisson disease*, popularly known as "the bends," a painful and damaging condition cause by the precipitation of minute nitrogen bubbles in the blood stream all over the body; severe cases are sometimes fatal.

It is of historical interest that the greatest pressure ever used in a caisson was during construction of the east pier of the St. Louis bridge (completed in 1874), before the cause of or treatment for "the bends" was known. The foundation of this pier was taken down to bedrock at the record depth of 38 m., using a final pressure of 3.43 kg/cm^2, considerably in excess of that normally permitted today.

Caissons are not necessarily used with compressed air, and today large caissons are usually constructed of a number of vertical cylindrical cells. After the water bed has been broken up (when necessary), the loose material is dredged out through the open-ended cylinders, the entire caisson remaining filled with water. The central anchorage pier of the San Francisco Bay bridge (diagramed on page 96) was built in this way. Here the depth of water was in any case too great for the use of compressed air in a working chamber; however, air was used in some of the cylinders fitted with top domes; this gave the caisson buoyancy while it was towed to the site, and aided its control during the sinking operation. When the caisson had been sunk through the soft

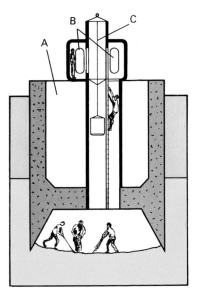

Section of a typical pneumatic caisson. When the caisson is sunk in position compressed air is pumped into the space below the deck (A) to prevent water from seeping up under the cutting edge through the soft bed. Men can then enter the pressurized chamber through air locks (B), and a separate air lock (C) is provided for conveying muck out and concrete in.

seabed by dredging through the open-ended cylinders, and when rock was reached, the rock surface was broken until a level footing had been made for the pier. This was done by dropping a 1000-kg. pointed steel bar or *gad* repeatedly through the open cylinders, the broken rock being removed by grab.

Underwater excavation and concreting, without the use of a caisson, was the method used to construct the foundation for the San Francisco Golden Gate bridge's south pier, the design of which is illustrated on page 000. For this difficult operation in 20 m. of seawater, a strong 30-m. access trestle was first constructed from the shore to the pier site. Strong enough to carry heavy dredging equipment and concrete plant, it was founded on temporary piles. Next an elliptical concrete breakwater, 90 m. × 45 m., was built around the pier site. This was keyed into bedrock, 5 m. of the rock being first excavated by deep-sea divers drilling, blasting, and dredging, during the four short daily periods of slack water—the tide making work impossible at other times.

It was originally intended to sink a 1,130,000 kg., 55 m. × 30 m. caisson inside the breakwater. This was built, and floated in through a gap left in the wall. Unfortunately a storm struck before the wall could be closed and the caisson was so severely damaged that it had to be towed out again and jettisoned. The engineer in charge immediately changed his plan. The breakwater was completed, its base cleaned of mud and silt, and 10 m. depth of concrete was poured on the rock inside it, under water. As soon as this had set the water was pumped out of the now watertight breakwater, the pier being completed inside it in the dry.

The comparatively new Prepakt system of underwater concrete placing (described briefly in Chapter 1) was used extensively in the foundation work of another great suspension bridge, the 1140-m. Mackinac bridge, which spans the neck between Lake Michigan and Lake Huron in the northern USA. This beautiful great bridge crosses deep water, the main towers founded on rock 60 m. below water level. Each of the main piers was built by first sinking a 35-m. double-walled steel caisson, the inner wall being tapered outward at its base to meet the outer wall and so form a cutting edge. When the caisson had been sunk into position in the overburden, its hollow, water-filled walls were packed with stone ranging in size from 2 to 12 cm. Then the special Prepakt cement mortar was pumped in, displacing the water between the stones to form concrete. The loose rock overburden was then dredged out of the middle of the caisson and as it sank deeper and deeper its walls were heightened by welding steel sections on top. When it had finally settled on rock its water-filled interior was packed with stone, which was then converted into concrete by the Prepakt method.

As we discovered in Chapter 4, underwater foundations based on piles driven or bored directly into the water bed are becoming increasingly common, even for large bridges. Such piles are placed by the usual methods, the plant being installed on barges where necessary. In the case of the mammoth job of driving piles into the seabed of Chesapeake Bay, USA, for the 20 km. of prestressed-concrete beams that are part of the Ocean Hiway bridge-tunnel crossing, a special rig was designed. Essentially a floating pile driver, it had stabilizer legs that were lowered to the seabed before each pile was driven. A second rig followed, leveling the tops of the piles and preparing them to receive the concrete beams.

The Construction of Beam Bridges

The new Tay road bridge in Scotland, completed in 1966, is a multispan bridge that is distinguished for its design simplicity. This bridge has 42 main spans, mostly of 54 m. All but four are made of two 4 m. × 3 m. steel box girders, prefabricated in a local workshop, and supported on two rows of elegant concrete piers, the height of the spans above water level varying from 6 m. at the north end to 32 m. near the south end. Here is the modern beam bridge par excellence.

The main erection problem was that of carrying construction loads of up to 200,000 kg. across the 2 km. of water, and of lifting the 84 heavy girders onto piers up to 32 m. high. The contractors solved this problem by building a low-level temporary bridge along the center line of the final bridge—there was sufficient room for this—with two narrow-gauge rail tracks, to run between the two rows of finished piers. This temporary bridge, founded on temporary steel-tube piles, was first used for driving the heavy H-section piles on which the main piers were founded, and for concreting these piers on site. Rail cars later carried each main girder between these piers where it was lifted, still between the columns, by a pair of special gantries erected over each pair of piers in turn. These gantries raised each girder above the top of the piers, traversed it, and lowered it into position on one side or the other.

This temporary light railroad bridge was an expensive piece of capital equipment on the project but the contractors reckoned that its many advantages, coupled with the likely resale value of its recovered material, more than justified the decision to build and use it. In any case the only alternative would have been to work from heavy pontoons; in an estuary where foul weather is not uncommon, the unscheduled delays might have been equally, possibly more, expensive. The problem of providing a navigation channel across the line of the temporary bridge during the construction period was solved by including in the line a double bascule, sited under one of the final navigation spans, which was

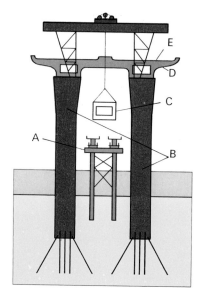

Section of the Tay road bridge during construction. A double-track temporary railroad (A) was erected the entire length of the bridge between the two rows of finished piers (B). A pair of especially constructed movable gantries were then used to shift the 84 steel box girders (C) to their final position (D) in which they support the roadway (E).

completed first to provide an overhead structure from which the bascule could be easily operated.

The erection of almost all multispan beam bridges consists essentially of the simple operation of carrying the beams or their component parts to the site, lifting them into position, and fixing them. Transport to suit the situation and lifting gear to suit the load generally provide the means. Where a bridge of this type is sufficiently low and the situation permits, scaffolding or falsework is sometimes used in the placing of beams, especially large trusses that can then be assembled in position from small components. Where concrete is to be poured on site, the falsework supports the formwork. In a multispan bridge of this type falsework for a limited number of spans can be used over the entire bridge by moving it successively along.

Ingenious methods of lifting and placing beams are sometimes used. When the new St. Lawrence Seaway was being opened up, the level of the 18 approach spans of the Jacques Cartier bridge to the south of St. Helen Island had to be raised bodily, the central 75-m. span by as much as 5 m., to give the 45-m. vertical clearance required for the Seaway. This difficult operation was carried out in the astonishingly short time of four hours, using especially designed hydraulic jacks. Helicopters have even been employed to place clusters of girders that make up short-span beam bridges in crowded city centers.

Barges sometimes provide the only means of tackling a difficult beam bridge erection project; a remarkable instance is the placing of the 50 steel spans of the Storstrom bridge, which links the Danish islands of Sjælland and Falster. The 47 side spans were plate girders varying in length from 53 to 61 m., weighing up to 500,000 kg. each. These had to be placed on piers 30 m. above water level. To do this job a huge 610,000-kg. floating crane was built with the aid of two gigantic steel barges that had seen 30 years' service carrying grain on the Elbe River.

The main navigation spans—tied arches—two of 101 m., one of 134 m., were too heavy even for this crane to handle. They were placed in position in parts, the crane first lifting the two bottom chords, which were supported at their centers on trestles. A smaller traveling crane was then placed across these girders and used to erect the arch ribs and hangers.

When the multispan Marshal Carmona bridge was built across the Tagus River in Portugal, the contractor was faced with the problem of placing five 610,000-kg. tied arches in position on their piers about 20 m. above water level. These spans were structurally unsuitable for erection by the cantilever method (described later in this chapter), and the situation was such that the erection of falsework would have been uneconomic. The problem was solved by the construction of a temporary steel service truss, 98 m. long, which was floated by pontoon and set, first between the first two piers, on shelves constructed for this purpose at the base of each pier.

Cantilever Bridge Construction

When a cantilever bridge is being erected, either the anchor arms must be completed first, so that the overhang of the cantilevers will not topple the bridge, or the cantilever arms and anchor arms must be built simultaneously so that the structure remains balanced on its pier. In the first alternative, falsework may be required because the anchor arm, designed to withstand tension in its top chord, will be differently stressed and may not have the strength to support itself, even temporarily, as a simple beam. Once the cantilever arms have been completed, either the intervening suspended span, if there is to be one, can be cantilevered out from each side of the gap until the halves meet and are joined, or the entire center span can be prefabricated and raised into position.

The cantilever arms of the Forth railway bridge (illustrated on page 112) were erected simultaneously on each side of their respective piers, the two suspended spans being built out from the ends of these arms. It is of interest to note that the engineer in charge had relied on the warm midday sun to heat the steel to the correct temperature for the two halves to meet perfectly at the time they were to be bolted together. But when one of these two suspended spans was to be joined, a cold northeast wind kept the east chord so much below the calculated temperature that the bolt holes did not coincide. As the west chord had already been bolted together it was vital that the east chord should also be joined before nightfall, when the general drop in temperature might seriously distort and buckle the unequally stressed span. With the courage that sometimes comes of panic the engineer immediately had wood shavings soaked in naphtha placed along the recalcitrant east chord, some 20 m. each side of the intended join, and put a match to it. The heat expanded the metal, closed the gap, and made it possible to insert the bolts.

When the first Quebec bridge failed during construction (collapsing in 1907 due to faulty design specifications) the center span was being built out from the two completed cantilever arms. Nine years later when the bridge was being rebuilt, the 192-m. 5,100,000-kg. center span was assembled on shore, floated to the bridge on pontoons, then lifted into position, using jacks.

On the first occasion this was attempted, a casting suffered an untimely failure, and the span buckled and crashed into the river, killing 13 men and injuring 14. But the plan was sound and when a new span had been built it was successfully hung in position by the same method.

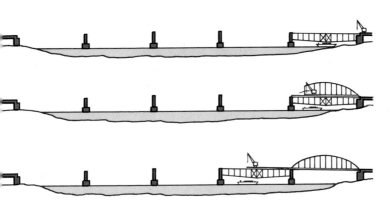

Method of erection used on the Marshal Carmona multispan beam bridge in Portugal. To avoid building expensive falsework, a temporary steel service span was placed between the first two piers by means of pontoons. The first main span was then erected above it, and the service span was moved on to the successive spans in turn as shown.

A more recent long-span cantilever construction was the 450-m.-span Howrah bridge at Calcutta, India, completed in 1943. Here the anchor arms were built first, supported by temporary scaffolding, and tied down to the anchorages. The cantilever arms were then erected, using creeper cranes working over the top of the bridge. Finally the suspended span was cantilevered out, half from each side, each half located 23 cm. back from its final position so that when complete a 46-cm. gap remained. Meanwhile eight 813,000-kg. hydraulic jacks had been built into the junction between each half span and the cantilever arm that supported it. When all was ready these 16 jacks were used to push out the two halves of the suspended span until they met and could be bolted together. Each half of this suspended span was 94 m. long and weighed 2 million kg. Linking them up high in the air over the center of the river was a feat of great precision. But it did not depend on temperature, since the device of incorporating the jacks gave the engineer the power to move the great half trusses exactly where and when he wished.

Incidentally, the Howrah bridge has the world's fourth longest cantilever span. After the Quebec and Forth bridges, third place is taken by the 479-m. New Orleans-Algiers bridge, Louisiana USA, completed in 1958.

The Medway prestressed-concrete cantilever bridge (illustrated on page 109) was built by casting the concrete box girders on site in 3-m. sections, working outward from the main piers in each direction. While the work was thus kept substantially in balance, the anchor arms, which are longer than the cantilevers, were cast one step ahead of the latter to avoid any possible risk of these toppling into the river. The slight additional weight retained on the anchor arm side was supported by light temporary steel trestles. Each 3-m. section was poured, allowed to set, and finally stressed, using longitudinal and vertical steel bars of 3-cm. diameter laid through ducts and subsequently grouted in. The grouting and steel, after stressing, was finally tested for soundness by gamma-ray photography.

The Building of Steel Arches

For thousands of years the classical arch bridge material was masonry and the classical construction method was building over falsework. The development of steel and concrete solved the problem of providing really strong bridges across much wider gaps, but created another. The very condition that justified the construction of a long steel arch (as opposed to a cheaper multispan bridge) often barred the use of falsework. If a multispan bridge was impracticable because the site was unsuitable for underwater pier foundations, it was probably equally unsuitable for constructing falsework. Or if navigation requirements demanded an unobstructed channel, falsework, which would cause a far greater obstruction than the piers of many bridges, would again be out of the question. One great steel arch, and only one, has been erected over falsework. It is the Bayonne bridge, New York—the longest of them all. Even here a navigation channel had to be, and indeed was, kept open. But for this one exception, all major steel arches have been built by the cantilever method already described.

Let us take a look at the erection of the Sydney Harbor bridge. The problem, briefly, was the existence of a 470-m. gap across the deep water of the harbor where falsework could not be used. The steel arch, designed to carry a 19-m. roadway and four interurban rail tracks, would weigh 38 million kg. and rest entirely on four bearings. The construction of the abutments, which have been described in Chapter 4, presented no problem and was completed while the components of the arch were being fabricated. Half the bridge was now built out over the water from each side, the two halves being held back during erection by stays, each made up of 128 steel-wire ropes, 7 cm. diameter, 360 m. long—100 km. of cable being used in all. These stays were attached to the ends of the upper chords of the arch halves by means of huge cradles at which every cable could be independently tightened or loosened by means of jacks. The complete set of cables from one cradle then passed back and downward to a U-shaped hole that had been tunneled 30 m. into the rock behind each abutment, providing a rock "eye" through which the cables were threaded, returning to a second cradle on the opposite side of the girder.

As soon as the first section of the arch was in position, supported by these cables, a 600,000-kg. creeper crane, capable of lifting 120,000 kg., was built on the top chord on bogies and used to lift the steelwork from barges and place it in position as the arch was built out, panel by panel, the crane hauling itself progressively toward the center of the span as required.

When the two half arches were complete there remained a gap of a few centimeters to be closed, as planned, by letting the retaining cables out gradually until the two halves met, a 20-cm.-diameter pointed steel peg or spigot fitting in a hole to center the girders accurately for bolting together. The method of letting down the immensely heavy bridge halves gradually is a simple process known as *fleeting*. The individual cables of the retaining stays were let out, one at a time, by a few centimeters. The increased tension in the remainder, when one cable was let out, caused all the others to stretch, thus lowering the arch halves by a fraction of a centimeter. A problem lay in the fact that the expansion and contraction of the steel, due to natural temperature changes, could open or close the gap as fast as was possible by fleeting the cables. The process had therefore to be done at a precise time of day when the rate of change of temperature could be accurately predicted.

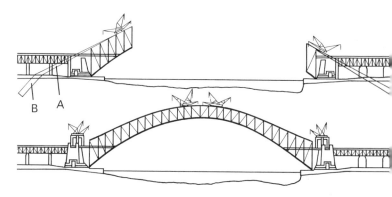

Erection of the Sydney Harbor bridge, Australia. First, half the steel arch was built out from each side, held back by steel wire cables (A) threaded through "eyes" in the rock (B) behind each abutment. A creeper crane was then built on the top chord of each side, and it constructed the rest of the two half arches, moving forward as it did so. Finally the remaining gap was closed by gradually letting out the steel cables.

Once the arch had been joined at the center, the retaining cables were removed, and the creeper cranes backed down the arch halves, erecting the steelwork of the deck and its hangers as they went. Finally the cranes were removed, the granite pylons and approaches completed, and the roadway and rail tracks laid.

While most steel arches are erected by the cantilever method, there are variations on this theme. The erection of the 324-m Birchenough bridge in Rhodesia was aided by the use of an aerial cableway from shore to shore. The parts of the girders were carried from one side on this ropeway and transferred in mid-air to the creeper cranes used for assembly. An interesting feature of this bridge's construction was the need for economy in transport, as the site was so far from the beaten track. In the event almost everything taken to the site was used in building the bridge, so that it need not be taken away. The erection cranes were made from parts of the bridge used in the final stage of construction—the roadway—and the cables used as stays during the cantilever construction phase were subsequently cut to length to form the roadway hangers. (In fact these cables were second-hand. They had earlier been used as the erection stays for the Sydney Harbor bridge.)

An important design feature of most large steel arches should now be self-evident. They must not only be strong enough to fulfil their role as arches when the bridge is complete, but must also be capable of supporting themselves, with their creeper cranes on their backs, during the cantilever stage of construction—a situation causing very different stresses in many of the arches' members.

The comparatively recent 242-m. Volta bridge, 100 km. north-east of Accra, Ghana, was built by the cantilever method, but with a new technique. The arch was designed as a series of high-tensile shop-welded steel sections, butted and bolted at each junction by four high-tensile steel bolts. Bolted joints made the girders less vulnerable during the tension stage of cantilever erection, when steel rivets are inclined to change shape permanently (creep) under the temporary tensile load. As a result considerable time and expense were saved.

Concrete Arches

As reinforced concrete is weak in tension, the cantilever method of construction is generally unsuited to arches of this material. In fact most of the world's large concrete arches are built on ground-supported falsework. In the case of the Gladesville bridge at Sydney, the four hollow 305-m.-span arch ribs were built on steel centering supported by tubular steel trestles founded on the river bed.

In this instance, to save expense on the centering, this was provided for one arch rib only, the four ribs being placed one after the other, and the centering moved across. These ribs were built up of precast sections weighing up to 50,000 kg. (depending on the varying arch depth). These were lifted from barges at the center span by a winch on a projection cantilevered from a temporary erection tower. The sections were lowered onto trolleys on the centering, then rolled into position. While most of the centering was of short-span beams, there was one 60-m. section, of lattice girder construction that bridged a gap left in the trestles to provide a permanent opening for shipping.

The three prestressed-concrete bridges on the Caracas Autopista (longest span 150 m., see Chapter 2) presented their designer,

Gladesville bridge, Sydney, in course of construction. Ground-supported false-work was built for only one of the four arch ribs at a time to save expense and a gap was left in the supporting trestles for the passage of shipping. In the photograph, two of the ribs are complete, and precast sections of the third are being hoisted from barges by a winch on a cantilevered projection.

the well-known French engineer Eugène Freyssinet, with the problem of building in concrete without ground-supported false-work. There were three reasons:

1. The roadway was to be some 70 m. above the bottom of each gorge;
2. The sides of the gorges were steep with a crumbly surface;
3. Cyclonic storms producing 160 km/h down-valley squalls were prevalent in the area.

Taken together, these three factors made falsework impracticable. If built, it would be so tall and uncertainly founded that it would probably not have withstood the full blast of a squall down the gorge. In any case it would necessarily have been so substantial as to prove uneconomic. Even the problem of bringing the material for such falsework through the mountainous country to the site would have been formidable and therefore costly.

Freyssinet's solution was ingenious, yet basically simple. The three box sections of each arch would be constructed in stages, starting with extremely light cantilevered formwork, placed by aerial ropeway, and strong enough to support itself and the concrete of just the thin lower chords of the arches. As soon as

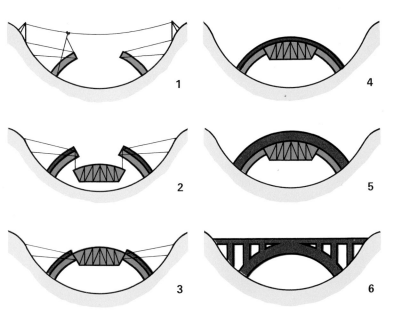

Method of constructing concrete bridges on Venezuela's Caracas Autopista. Because ground-supported falsework was impracticable for several reasons, the work was done in stages. Light formwork was cantilevered out and the lower chord built on each side (1). This was then strong enough for a light wooden trussed arch to be raised (2) and wedged in the center (3), and the lower chord was then completed (4). The rib and upper chord of each arch was then constructed (5), the wooden arch removed, and the rest of the bridge completed (6). Below: one of the bridges when finished.

these chords had set, they would provide sufficient additional strength to support the next stage of construction, which in turn would support the third. In practice the cantilevered formwork could only be built out for a quarter of the span on each side. To bridge the intervening gap, after the lower chords of the two quarter spans had been poured and had set, a light wooden trussed arch was assembled in the bed of the gorge, winched into position, and wedged between the existing formwork of the two quarter spans. Pouring of the lower chords of the box sections was now completed. As soon as this had hardened, the combined strength of the concrete and timber formwork was sufficient to support the additional formwork and concrete for the webs, and this in turn made possible the pouring of the much more substantial top chords. The construction of the main road slab and its supports then presented no difficulty.

As this method of construction, which was entirely new at the time, used the combined strength of the thin lower chords and their formwork to support subsequent loads, accurate knowledge was required of the stresses involved, which depended on two inadequately known factors—the effective friction between the concrete and the wood, and the difference in their elasticity. In order to overcome this lack of precise knowledge and to check the calculations, a 1:5 scale model of a section of the partly constructed arch was built in Paris, and loaded to ascertain its strength. The deflection in the model, under full load, was 1 cm., corresponding to 5 cm. in the completed bridge. Survey measurements made during the building of the bridge showed that the actual deflection was exactly 5 cm., proving the reliability of the technique of checking stresses by the use of a scale model.

The Construction of Suspension Bridges

The erection of modern long-span suspension bridges has become a largely standardized engineering exercise, in which there are four distinct steps:
1. Construction of the tower and anchorage foundations;
2. Erection of the towers;
3. Fabrication and placing in position of the main cables;
4. Assembly of the roadway.

Having built the foundations as already described, the towers must next be erected. Owing to the tower's great height and the immense weight it has to carry, the base of a suspension bridge tower must be exceptionally strong and accurately level. The erection of the Golden Gate bridge towers was typical. First the concrete pier tops were ground and leveled to within 0.4 cm. Onto this bed were placed 12.5-cm.-thick slabs of steel, fixed to the concrete by means of 2-cm.-diameter steel dowels, welded to the slabs. The surfaces of these slabs were now ground until level, this time to an accuracy of within 0.75 mm. Then the lowest sections of the cellular towers were welded directly to the prepared slabs, with angles added for additional strength.

Once the lower part of each leg of a tower was established an especially designed platform was fitted between them. This steel platform incorporated hydraulic gear by which it could climb between the tower legs as they were extended upward, and was strong enough to support two cranes, one to raise the steel for each leg. The legs were built up 15 m. at a time, the sections being welded in place.

This system of tower erection, using a climbing crane, is normal, though minor variations are found in the design of the cranes and their platforms. In the case of the recently completed Forth suspension bridge, the crane platform was in the form of a ring entirely surrounding the two legs of the tower. It carried one 32,000-kg. crane. The platform was raised (and eventually lowered) by means of hydraulic jacks.

We have seen already how the main cables of large suspension bridges consist of a mass of high-tensile steel wires, the overall diameter of each cable measuring as much as 1 meter. We have also seen how these cables are of two types: one made up of thousands of individual wires, all laid parallel; the other of a bunch of twisted steel-wire ropes.

The procedure for spinning cables from individual wires is, like so many engineering processes, remarkably simple. The wire arrives at the site in reels that may hold, on average, 1200 m. of wire. First this wire is rewound onto giant reels holding as much as 48,000 m., the joins being carefully spliced in such a way that the strength of the joint is not more than 5 per cent less than the

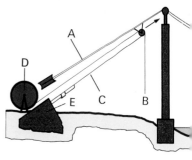

Above: method of spinning suspension bridge cables from individual wires. A continuous cable (A) is erected and a fixed carriage (B) with a grooved wheel is hauled to and fro pulling a loop of wire (C) across the span, unwinding from a reel (D) and attached by one end to the cable anchorage (E). At the other bank, the loop is taken off and affixed, a fresh wire placed on the wheel, and the process repeated in reverse. Left: spinning in progress on the Verrazano-Narrows suspension bridge. Opposite: one of the great cable anchorages before spinning.

strength of the wire. A fixed cable is now set up so that a carriage can run along it, supported by pulleys; it runs from one anchorage, over the towers, and down to the opposite anchorage. The carriage is attached to a second (endless) moving cable by which it can be hauled back and forth like the cars on a mountain cableway.

On the carriage are a number of large, free-running, grooved wheels; the wire from one of the large reels at one anchorage is attached to a nearby clamp or shoe, the resulting loop being passed around one of the grooved wheels. When the carriage is hauled across to the opposite side, a pair of parallel wires is thus run out behind it. When the crossing is complete, these wires are checked for level and sag, and the loop is then pulled off the grooved wheel and passed around another shoe. A fresh wire from a reel on this bank is now placed around the grooved wheel and the process is repeated in reverse, resulting in 4 wires placed by one grooved wheel in one double journey. If there are three such wheels on the carriage, a double pass will lay 12 wires; and since

two carriages are made to run simultaneously in opposite directions, the complete double round trip lays 24 wires.

When all the wires for the main cable have been laid by this process, the huge bundle is compacted by a machine that travels along the cable, binding it around the circumference with wire as it goes. Coats of corrosion-resistant paint are applied first below and finally over the binding wire.

To make this process workable, men must have access to the cable throughout the spinning and binding process. For this purpose a long catwalk is first constructed; it consists of cross timbers supported on light cables and is adjusted to hang a meter or so below the curve of the completed main cable.

This system of cable spinning has been used on two of the most recently completed long-span suspension bridges (the new Forth bridge in Scotland and the Severn bridge across the estuary dividing England and Wales); an alternative method of laying parallel wires has been used on at least one notable bridge, the 300-m. Otto Beit suspension bridge designed by Sir Ralph

Freeman to span the Zambezi River, and completed in 1939. In this case the cables were made up of 40 layers, each layer being a ribbon of wires cut to size and laid parallel side by side. These ribbons were made up on shore and pulled across the river in one piece. Instead of strand shoes at each end the ribbons were fitted into cast steel sockets and cemented with white metal.

A recent example of the use of twisted steel-wire ropes for a large suspension bridge is in the 610-m. Tancarville bridge over the Seine. Each of its main cables consists of 60 steel-wire ropes of about 7 cm. diameter, weighing 28,000 kg. These ropes were hauled across the river and up and over the towers, one at a time, supported meanwhile on a series of rollers hung at 10-m. intervals from an overhead service cable. A work car suspended from another service cable provided access for compacting the ropes and bolting on the support bands that were to hold the roadway suspenders. This method of placing the main cables avoided the costly temporary catwalks and the reeling and unreeling machinery required by the American spinning system, but necessitated the handling of much greater weights across the 610 m. of open water. Steps taken against corrosion on the Tancarville cables included their immersion in a tar-based paint immediately after manufacture, and the application of more paint after assembly on the bridge.

Erection of the road deck of a suspension bridge is done from each end of the bridge, either by working along the deck surface as it is laid, or by lifting prefabricated sections floated into position on the water below. In the case of the new Severn bridge the latter method was used, and because the sections were watertight and buoyant they could be floated directly to the site without the need for supporting rafts or barges.

Either method of erection results in distortion of the bridge in the early stages as, until the deck is complete at the middle, the dead weight at the ends is relatively greater. Consequently the main cable rises slightly at its lowest middle point and the towers bend slightly shoreward. Due to this distortion the lower chords of the stiffening trusses (which form part of the structure of most such bridges) cannot be connected until the roadway is complete and the bridge has returned to its correct shape. This makes the bridge somewhat unstable and vulnerable to wind forces while the deck is partly built. Additional temporary bracing is usually fitted as a precaution against oscillation caused by winds.

In this chapter we have seen how bridge foundations are built, sunk to bedrock if possible. We have seen how beams are laid, and how trusses may be fabricated in position, using falsework. We have seen how cantilevers can be built out from one bank, and how arches can be erected by the same method, using stays to convert the halves of the arch into temporary cantilevers. And finally we have seen how the towers, steel cables, and decks of great suspension bridges are constructed. But above all, we have seen again and again how the construction of great bridges makes demands upon the ingenuity of the bridge builder—demands perhaps greater, and certainly more varied, than those made in any other sector of civil engineering.

6 The Technique of Tunneling

The first tunnel in recorded history, like the first great bridge, was built by the Babylonians. Probably constructed in about 2160 B.C., this remarkable achievement passed under the river Euphrates at a spot not far from the bridge carrying the public road. It was, however, a small private tunnel, built for the king's own use, to provide him with a short cut from the royal palace to a temple on the other side. Road tunnels were built by the Incas to carry their roads through otherwise impassable barriers of mountain rock, but most early road-builders had no use for tunnels. In difficult country the roads were simply sited along valleys, winding up and over mountain passes.

When the pioneer civil engineers of the 18th century began to link the existing river-transport routes with canals the need for tunnel engineering quickly arose. Canals, to contain water, must be level. Often a cutting served to link waterways on the opposite sides of higher ground, but sometimes the ridge was too high for a cutting, yet tantalizingly narrow. Tunnels provided the answer.

Four-decked drilling jumbo used on the Italian side of the 12-km. automobile tunnel under Mont Blanc, completed in 1965. Eighteen tungsten-carbide-tipped drills were used to place rounds of charges, and in ideal conditions daily progress of up to 10 meters was averaged at full section. This jumbo was subsequently destroyed by a roof fall.

The first known canal tunnel was completed in 1777, on the Grand Trunk Canal, England, and was 2.7 km. long, 3 m. wide, and 4 m. high. Once the pattern was set canal tunnels began to appear all over Europe and America. But hardly had the new fashion become a necessary engineering facility for the canal builders than the railway age burst upon an excited 19th-century world, and tunneling became primarily the railway engineer's art. Not that canal tunneling had ended for ever; as recently as 1927 the world's largest bore canal tunnel was opened. This 7.2-km. shaft was a splendid 24 m. wide and 36 m. high and was filled with water to a depth of 20 m.; it connected the French port of Marseilles with the river Rhône.

When, in the 19th century, the railroads began to spread across Europe and America, natural obstacles and the severe limits to the hill-climbing ability of the early steam locomotives made extensive tunnel-building essential. With few exceptions, the problems of those early days are the problems of today and one can only look back with deep admiration at the French engineer who settled in England, Sir Marc Brunel (father of the better known Isambard Kingdom Brunel) who in 1824 invented a fantastic cast-iron and timber tunneling shield, and proceeded calmly to drive under the river Thames what is to this day one of the largest bore under-river tunnels ever built. His fabulous Thames tunnel, which is still in constant use by the London Underground system, is 353 m. long, and consists of two parallel 5-m.-high brick-lined vaulted archways, each 5 m. across at carriageway level. (More about this tunnel will be found in Chapter 7.)

Equally impressive was the cool nerve of the French and Italian engineers of 1857 who set out with hand drills and black powder to bore a tunnel through almost 12 kilometers of Alpine granite that lay between them under Mont Cenis. At first progress was slower than even they had anticipated with their cautious if audacious enthusiasm—22 centimeters a day at each end; so slow that, as a brief calculation will show, the tunnel could only have been completed by their grandsons, even if nothing had gone wrong! Fortunately for them the compressed-air drill had recently been invented by Germain Sommeiller, an Italian engineer. With the aid of a water-powered compressor, these drills were introduced at Mont Cenis in 1861, working 10 at a time on a 8 m. × 2 m. × 2 m. "jumbo"—a form of carriage that moved on rails inside the tunnel. Soon dynamite replaced gunpowder and tunneling speed increased to 2 m. a day. The finished brick- and stone-lined shaft, accommodating a double-line railroad, was opened in 1871.

Tunneling in Rock

Today, most hard-rock tunnels are bored by an almost identical process, though the drilling and soil-disposal equipment is more sophisticated, and very much more efficient. The rock face is first attacked by drilling a pattern of holes using compressed-air rock drills working at pressures as high as 5–6 kg/cm^2 or even higher. The air supply and the water for cooling are piped to the working face by pressure hose suspended from hooks let into the crown of the tunnel, thus getting them out of the way of the mine railroad and other equipment. The compressors and pumps are usually sited outside the nearest portal or access shaft.

With today's tungsten-carbide bits a modern rock drill can penetrate 2–3 m. in 4–5 minutes. A number of drills are operated simultaneously from the various levels of the modern jumbo, which has built-in ring mains for the compressed air and water supplies, several outlets being conveniently placed at each level. The pattern, depth, and direction of the holes drilled depends on the size and shape of the tunnel and on the type of rock. As soon as a round of holes has been completed, high explosive—usually a form of dynamite—is packed in and fused, again according to a prearranged pattern. The charges in the central holes will detonate first, those round it following successively, one, two, three, or more seconds later, the charges near the tunnel's circumference exploding last.

As soon as the charges have been laid and fused the jumbo is hauled back to a parking bay, probably by diesel or electric loco-motive, and the men retire to a safe distance. The charges are fired electrically, after which there is a pause in the routine to allow the smoke and fumes to clear. The process is aided by the compressed-air supply, which now feeds a large volume of fresh air to the face, ventilating the whole tunnel by displacement.

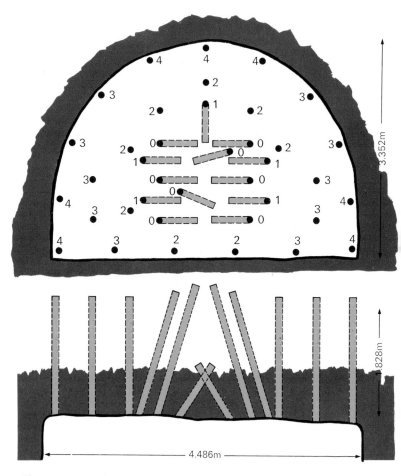

Above: cross section and plan of a typical drilling pattern for a tunnel through rock. The figures indicate the number of seconds delay allowed for in the fuses for the various charges to ensure accurate and even loosening of the rock. Below: plant for rapid removal of rock after blasting, showing rock shovel (A), shuttle car with steel slat conveyor-belt floor (B), and diesel locomotive (C). With a machine of this kind, the drill-blast-clear cycle can be as short as 35 minutes.

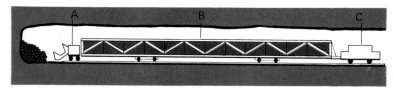

When the smoke has cleared completely—this may take 20–30 minutes—the men move in again, this time with rock-handling plant. A mobile rock shovel, especially designed for tunnel work and probably working on compressed air, lifts the broken rock and deposits it in dump cars, which are hauled away by a compact locomotive, on rails laid for them.

This removal of the broken rock from the working face is the main obstacle to high-speed tunneling through rock—obviously the spoil must all be cleared away before the jumbo can be brought back. Experimental work continues constantly to find ways of speeding rock removal, and new equipment is always under development in various parts of the world. In a small-bore tunnel (2 m. wide × 3 m. high) cut through granite a few years ago in Scotland, a special shuttle car was designed to carry the debris from a complete blasting "round" 2–3 m. deep. This car was 21 m. long, supported on two eight-wheel bogies. Its floor consisted of a steel-slat conveyor belt running on rollers and propelled by hydraulic rams. A rail-mounted rock shovel was used to discharge broken rock onto the front end of the shuttle-car conveyor belt which moved it slowly along toward the rear. As soon as the rock had all been cleared and the conveyor belt was loaded to capacity, the entire shuttle car was hauled away to a spot beyond the jumbo parking siding where it could discharge its load at leisure into waiting mine cars. This system speeded up the task of clearing the face so dramatically that the drill-blast-clear cycle was reduced to about 35 minutes; in one remarkable week this particular heading was driven 133 m., probably a world record. Incidentally the conveyor belt rams were powered by a hydraulic pump built into the shuttle car's own locomotive, which could be operated and driven by remote control from the front end of the 21-m. car.

Owing to the high cost of carbide-tipped bits for rock drills, "throwaway" bits are sometimes used. These untipped bits are discarded after drilling a single hole. In certain rocks this proves cheaper than using the more sophisticated tipped bits.

Rock Tunneling by Machine

In recent years automatic tunneling machines that cut their way through soft rock have been used with increasing success. One such machine, probably the world's largest, cut five 9-m.-diameter tunnels through 540 m. of sandstone and limestone during the building of Pakistan's Mangla dam project in 1963. A 7-km. tunnel, 5 m. in diameter, was driven by a similar machine during the construction of the Great Lake power project in Tasmania the same year. The USSR, too, has advanced tunneling-machine design. One, used on the 7 kilometers added to the Moscow Metro since 1959, bores a 6-m.-diameter hole 7 m. each six-hour shift.

Meanwhile an American firm that had earlier perfected a remarkable coalmining machine designed and built a hard-rock tunneling machine on the same principle. This machine, which weighed 72,000 kg., first drilled a 44-cm. pilot hole, 3 m. deep, the rock cuttings being removed by compressed air through the center of the huge bit. Next a set of steel grips were extended in the front 0.6 m. of the pilot hole, gripping it securely by outward pressure. Finally the 4-m. cutter head, which had 53 rolling cutters, was rotated by a 450 KW hydraulic motor, moving forward into the rock under the action of 450,000-kg. thrust developed by pulling on the pilot anchor. The cuttings were automatically scooped from the tunnel invert, dropped into a chute, and thus fed to a conveyor. It will be noticed that this machine did not have to rely on the tunnel lining to withstand the required forward thrust. In a hard-rock tunnel, where a lining may not be needed, this would be an unnecessary expense; and even where a lining was provided it might not be economical to build it strong enough to stand the very great thrust required for the machine to cut through the harder rocks.

The machine tried out its teeth, so to speak, on a projected 4-m.-diameter, 8-km. water tunnel through solid rock under the Upper Bay between Brooklyn and Staten Island, New York. Unfortunately it proved unreliable and the tunnel was completed in 1965 by conventional blasting methods. But I described the machine in some detail to illustrate how engineers are at work developing new ideas to solve specific problems. A successful hard-rock tunneling machine is inevitable. It is only a question of time and money.

As we have seen, tunnels in firm solid rock sometimes need no lining; but where faults or soft strata are found, lining becomes essential. In the early rock tunnels masonry was used, jointed with lime or cement mortar. Today concrete is usual, the mix being pumped under pressure behind suitable formwork until the entire gap is filled. In early railroad tunnels the sulfur in the smoke of coal-burning locomotives caused deterioration to the cement mortar normally used with masonry or bricks, and to early concrete linings. The replacement of steam railroad engines by diesel and electric-powered locomotives has virtually eliminated this problem, though special linings may sometimes be necessary where the rock fissures carry salt-laden water.

Survey by Pilot Tunnel

The cutting of a small pilot tunnel along the line of a planned major tunnel is normal practice and the information gained about the rock strata may make substantial design and construction savings possible later. And since even "solid" rock is rarely homogenous a pilot tunnel often proves worth the extra expense involved.

The traditional method of surveying by pilot bore is simple. Small boreholes (say 5 cm.-diameter) are drilled forward through the face of the pilot tunnel, up through its roof and to each side. The hardness of the rock can thus be estimated in advance, and

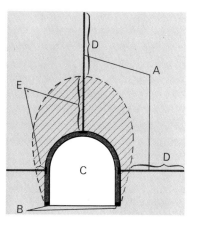

Rock survey using extensometers (A) and load cells (B) in a pilot tunnel (C). Strain readings indicating compression (D) and tension (E) supplied by extensometers suggest the estimated tension zone indicated by shading. Load cells measure pressure on steel arch ribs (gray).

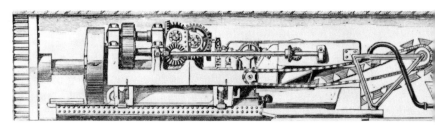

The Beaumont rotary clay-tunneling machine of 1882. Driven by compressed air, this machine bored a 2-m.-diameter tunnel through clay under the English Channel at a rate of 5 cm. an hour. Only the timidity of the British government of the day prevented completion of the tunnel by this means.

the material drilled out is examined to obtain advance information of the existence of faults in the rock. Any inflow of water is, of course, accurately measured.

Recently, in the United States, a new form of instrumentation was developed for more accurate pilot-tunnel survey work. Here 8-m. boreholes are drilled vertically into the roof and horizontally to each side of the pilot tunnel at suitable intervals—say 60 m. Into each hole a form of extensometer is fitted. This is designed to measure the strain in the rock as the pilot bore advances— whether the rock is in compression or tension, and to what extent—so that the required strength of the main tunnel lining can be accurately calculated, permitting savings where the rock is

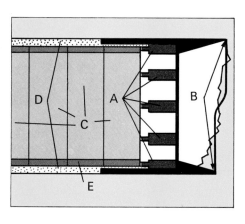

Longitudinal cross section of a typical clay-tunneling shield, showing hydraulic rams (A), cutting edge (B), steel lining segments (C), and the annular gap filled with cement grout (D). Note the projecting hood of the cutting edge to protect miners from falling debris.

found to be firm, and ensuring safety with economy where there are faults or other weaknesses. Sometimes, in addition to the extensometers, load cells are placed under the temporary pilot tunnel roof supports, providing a direct measurement of the rock pressure in the crown of the tunnel. (A load cell is an instrument in which a resistance bridge circuit provides an electrical output proportional to the load resting on it, due to the strain induced in the resistance wire.) Where the rock is found to be unusually unstable, additional extensometers may be fitted in the region of faults, to estimate more accurately the "tension zone" in the rock.

Tunneling through Clay

Tunneling through clay has been likened to cutting through cheese. And though a great deal of early tunneling on soft ground has been done by men digging by hand inside a shield, engineers have been dreaming up automatic tunneling machines for use in soil, sand, and clay for almost a century.

When Sir Edward Watkins started work on a tunnel under the English Channel between England and France in 1882 he began by driving a 2.3-m.-diameter pilot heading from a shaft near Dover, using a rotary tunneling machine designed and built by a military engineer, Colonel Beaumont. Driven by compressed air, this machine cut through the under-Channel clay at a rate of 50 cm. an hour—a remarkable 12 m. every 24 hours. Watkins had pushed well over a mile southwards and his tunnel was already under the sea when Prime Minister Gladstone, in response to hysterical popular fears in Britain that such a tunnel would be an invitation to attack from Europe, ordered Sir Edward Watkins to stop work.

Though Beaumont's machine worked, it was unreliable, and it was the Greathead shield, a direct descendent of Marc Brunel's invention, that became the most vital piece of equipment used by clay and sand tunnelers for many decades. First used to drive London's 450-m.-long, 3-m.-diameter Tower Subway in 1869, this shield in its simplest form is a steel cylinder of the same diameter as the intended tunnel. It has a sharp cutting edge and the rib inside it is strong enough to withstand the immense force required to push it forward through earth or clay. Many Greathead shields were used on the construction of the City and South London railway in 1886, with hydraulic rams exerting a thrust of 385,000 kg., advancing at a rate of 4 m. every 24 hours.

The tunnel lining, normally made of prefabricated cast-iron segments, bolted together, is of slightly smaller outside diameter than the shield's inside dimension, so that it can be assembled within the "tail" of the shield. Between the front edge of the last segment and the shield's interior rib, hydraulic rams are fitted. By operating these the shield is driven forward into the ground, the rams pushing against the fitted tunnel lining. When the shield has moved forward the breadth of a lining segment (say 60 cm.) the ram heads, now extended, are withdrawn and a further ring of segments fitted. Meanwhile men dig away the 60 cm. of soil that has entered the head of the shield, using aids such as pneumatic picks and shovels and tipping it into mine cars in which it is taken away. By varying the ram pressures on opposite sides of the shield it can be made to move in a curve, varying gradients being achieved by similarly differentiating top and bottom ram pressures. Especially shaped segments are used for lining the tunnel at bends. In practice the shield has a projecting hood, its top cutting edge overhanging the base by about 50 cm. in order to minimize the risk of the ground falling in onto the miners.

The reader will have noticed that, at least in theory, an annular gap is left between the outside of the tunnel lining and the surface of the hole cut by the shield. In damp clay, which stands up for some time unsupported, this is definitely the case, and to prevent subsequent settlement of the ground above, this gap must be filled. The method used is injection of cement-water grout through threaded holes in the cast-iron lining, the holes being finally closed permanently with screw-in plugs.

When 5.5-m.-diameter shields were used to drive the Fulton Street tunnel under East River, New York, the propulsion of the shield was by eighteen 25-cm.-diameter rams, each working at a pressure of 420 kg/cm² and producing a total horizontal thrust of 4 million kg.

All manner of refinements have been made to the basic shield system of soft-rock tunneling. I have mentioned pneumatic shovels that aid in muck shifting. Another modern tool is the

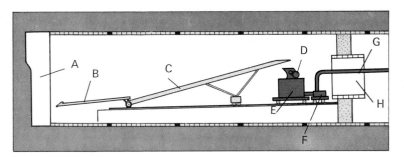

Layout of slurry-pumping plant for the disposal of spoil, showing shield (A), duck-bill loader (B), conveyor belt (C), crusher motor (D), mixing tank (E), pump (F), slurry-pumping main pipe (G), and air lock for men and equipment (H).

hydraulic bolt tightener that speeds the fitting of the cast-iron segments, and gives the bolts a permanent holding stress of up to 3500 kg/cm^2.

A shield with a face that is closed except for a number of rectangular openings (again, Marc Brunel's idea brought up to date) is used for tunneling through silt, which is "squeezed" in through the openings, like toothpaste, straight into disposal cars, as the shield is thrust forward.

Mechanized spoil-handling plant of varied and sometimes complex design, making use of conveyor belts, shuttle cars, and the like, has replaced much, though by no means all, of the human muscle still required. For placing the lining segments in position there is a compressed-air segment erector; it has an extending hydraulic arm that rotates about the axis of the tunnel. It can lift and place segments accurately in any required position, ready for bolting. Another machine grades excavated gravel, selecting only those pieces of pea-size; a stream of this gravel is then ejected by compressed air through an armored hose into the air-space around the tunnel lining, compacting it tightly so that the volume of cement grout needed to fill the gap is greatly reduced. The grout, too, is prepared by a specially designed machine. Another development is the use of slurry pumping for the disposal of spoil, as shown in the diagram on this page. This machine carries the spoil dug out by miners along a shaker-conveyor to a hammer

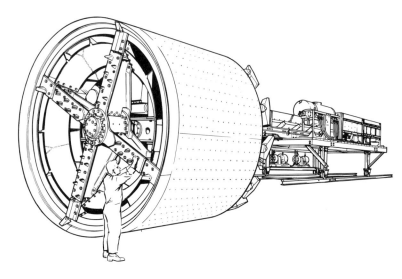

crusher that reduces all lumps to a maximum diameter of about 2.5 cm. The crushed material is next mixed with water to form a 5 per cent suspension, which is pumped out of the tunnel.

Research on uses for reinforced concrete has resulted in a prefabricated system suitable for lining tunnels. Already used in New York, this system has achieved savings of up to 35 per cent compared with the cost of lining in cast iron.

The most recent large tunneling project in clay is the boring of the 4.8 km. twin tunnels of the new Victoria Line for the London Underground system, where two new types of automatic soft-rock tunneling machines are in use, the drum-digger and the McAlpine. The latter, working within a conventional cylindrical shield, has a 4-m.-diameter star cutting wheel that revolves slowly at the working face of a cylindrical shield, powered by a slow-speed high-torque hydraulic motor. Hydaulic rams propel the entire machine forward in the traditional manner. Behind the cutting face and shield the machine has its power pack, a control console, and a conveyor belt that collects spoil directly from the working face, delivering it into skips behind the machine. Also incorporated in the rear is the machine's own hydraulic segment erector, which handles the tunnel lining segments, in this case of concrete.

Opposite: the McAlpine soft-rock tunneling machine. The 4-m.-diameter cutting wheel revolves slowly, powered by a low-speed, high-torque hydraulic motor. The photograph shows a workman placing wedges between the concrete lining segments, which are automatically positioned by an extension arm of the machine as it advances. The control platform of the machine can be seen in the background.

The prefabricated reinforced concrete segments are of a new design that requires no bolting or grouting, saving considerable time and enabling the machine to dig at its full rate without the lining lagging behind. Initially, these segments form an adjustable cylyndrical ring that fits inside the tail of the shield. As soon as the machine has moved on the ring is expanded by means of jacks and wedges until it fits tight against the clay face. While being expanded each ring automatically interlocks with the previous ring.

Tunneling under Water

The principal complication that upsets the routine of making tunnels, through either rock or soft ground, is the presence of water. Solid rock is, of course, impervious to water, but even solid rock frequently contains water-bearing fissures, sometimes deep geological bands of gravel or sand. In addition, water thus present in rock is often under considerable pressure.

The methods of dealing with subterranean water have been touched on in Chapter 1. Pressure grouting with either cement, bituminous emulsions, or gelling salt solutions can often solve the problem. Collection of the incoming water in a small reservoir and pumping it out may be necessary as a temporary expedient while a waterproof lining is being fitted. When the engineer sets out to tunnel under a river or the sea, his planning must take into account the possibility of a major inflow of water, and this may well influence the entire nature of his work, unless, which is unlikely, the subaqueous stratum through which the tunnel is to be bored is positively known to be totally impervious. Where inflow of water is considered likely there are a number of different methods of dealing with the problem. When Marc Brunel built his Thames tunnel, he relied on steam pumping.

There are two main methods used today for underwater tunneling. The traditional method is to raise the pressure of the air in the tunnel until it exceeds that of the water, the work of digging going on under pressure. This is similar to the method of sinking bridge foundations by pneumatic caisson. The newer method, which purists might argue is not tunneling at all, is to prefabricate sections of the tunnel on dry land and then lower them

Method of chemically injecting gravel to form a watertight barrier. The diagram shows temporary jetties (A) and the layers of silt (B) and water-filled gravel (C). The gravel on each side of the line of the tunnel (large black circle) was made watertight by injecting it with a bentonite-silicate-cement mixture to form an impervious ribbon (D).

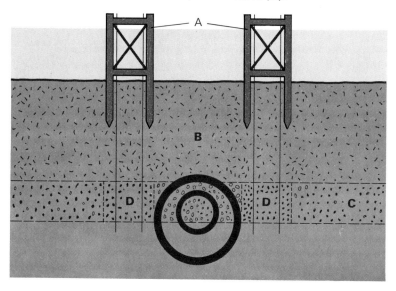

into a trench dredged in the water bed, the joints being subsequently waterproofed.

Where the pressure system is to be used in a conventional tunneling operation the procedure is as follows. The heading of the tunnel, which has not yet been given its permanent watertight lining, is sealed by means of heavy airtight gates having airlocks for the passage of men, materials, and spoil. All the equipment to be used for cutting the tunnel is within this pressure chamber. Air is now pumped into the sealed portion of the tunnel until the pressure exceeds that of the water in the ground, in this way keeping it out. Men work in the pressurized section of the tunnel, using all the usual equipment and aids (shield, conveyor, dump cars, segment erector) and so the tunneling proceeds. The same precautions must be taken as in caisson work to protect the men's health, and it is usual to build an independent decompression chamber in which the men rest and drink coffee while being slowly decompressed. Underwater tunnels have been built by this method all over the world, including most of those that carry London's Underground Railway below the Thames and those under New York's East River.

Incidentally the slurry method of spoil disposal referred to earlier is especially suitable for use in pressurized tunnel workings since it obviates the delays and costly waste of compressed air when loaded muck wagons have to pass through what is necessarily a very large air lock.

Water-bearing gravel is sometimes encountered in underwater tunneling, and due to its loose nature pressure work is hazardous, since too much compressed air is lost through the gravel. Such was the case when engineers came to drive a 10-m.-diameter road tunnel under the Thames at Dartford, east of London, in 1939, for though much of the tunnel was to run through impervious "blue" clay, it had to pass through a water-filled gravel bed under the river. The method used to beat this obstacle is particularly interesting and is shown in the diagram on page 150. A section of the gravel layer to each side of the line of the tunnel was made virtually airtight by converting it into an impervious ribbon—a bentonite-silicate-cement mixture was injected through the river bed from above. Tubes were pushed into the river bed from tem-

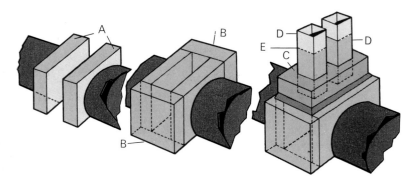

Method of joining sections of the Paris Metro under the Seine. Sections (red) were sunk in the mud with about 2 m. between them. End and side walls (A and B) were then sunk enclosing a mud core on four sides. A steel roof (C) was then placed upon the walls, and sealed with rubber or clay (black), and mud and water was removed through shafts (D) extending above water level (E). The sections were then joined by men working in this sealed-off box or cofferdam.

porary jetties, and the stabilizing mixture was pumped down through these tubes which were fitted with non-return valves. This process was entirely successful.

The Immersed-Tube System

The tunnels, completed in 1910, that carry the Paris Metro under the river Seine were built in what was then a most unusual way. The Paris Metro system, which is not a deep tube, was laid mostly by the method of cut and cover. A huge trench was dug; the tunnel casing was then built inside it and finally covered in with the original spoil from the trench. Where the Metro was to cross the river it was necessary to site the underwater tunnels no deeper than absolutely necessary. In fact the tops of these tunnels lie hardly a meter below the river bed.

To build these tunnels the engineers used the principle of the modern immersed-tube tunnel, combined with that of the pneumatic caisson. Huge metal sections of the tunnel were prefabricated and sunk, end to end, in dredged trenches. But a 2-m.-gap was left between the end of one section and the next. (The sections averaged 30 m. in length; two were needed for some crossings, three for others; the Seine is not a wide river.)

At each junction a box was built underwater, two of its sides forming temporary end walls to the tubes, the other two running parallel to the length of the tunnel. The enclosed space was then extended upward through the water with metal shafts to form, in effect, narrow cofferdams from which the water was pumped and the mud excavated. The boxes between the tube ends, now clear of mud, were next roofed over just below the level of the river bed. The main tunnel tubes were then pressurized, and miners, working under pressure, opened up the walls of the boxes forming the

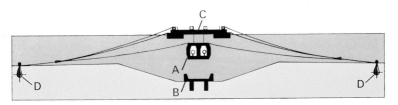

Below: method of lowering prefabricated tunnel section (A) onto foundation piles (B) in a dredged channel in the Ij River, Holland. Winches on board the raft (C) attached to tunnel section and pile anchors (D) are used to keep the section in position during sinking. Photograph shows a section of the Coen tunnel, Amsterdam, arriving at the sinking area. In this case, sinking buoys were located at all four corners, and the section held in place by tugs.

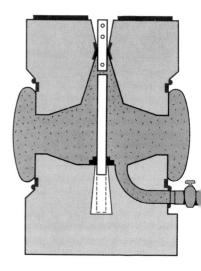

Cross section of adjustable-top pilehead used in sinking the Rotterdam Metro, Holland. To ensure that all piles are level and the load equally distributed, a nylon-skinned cavity (yellow) is filled with cement grout through an injection pipe when the section is in position. As the pressure of grout is the same for each pilehead, the weight of the tunnel section is equally shared.

ends of the tubes, built floors to the boxes, and rendered the whole construction waterproof.

The principle of the immersed tube has lately been developed to a fine art. Tunnel sections, made of concrete or steel or a combination of both, are prefabricated, preferably in a dry dock adjoining the site of the tunnel. They are then floated to their final position where a foundation has been prepared by dredging a trench in the water bed and, usually, by driving piles. The tunnel sections are sunk into position, end to end, their temporary end walls opened up and the joints made watertight. Finally the trench is filled in, giving the tunnel added stability. While prefabricated tunnel sections are today often 60 m. or more in length and consequently extremely heavy, the buoyancy given them by the enclosed air carries most of their weight both before and after sinking, with the result that suitable pile foundations are not difficult to provide.

The main problem in providing the pile foundations is that of ensuring that the tops of all the piles are accurately leveled so that the load from the rigid tunnel sections will be equally distributed. In building the new Metro in Rotterdam, Holland, now nearing completion, the problem has been ingeniously solved. A tunnel section is first lowered onto two pairs of piles one quarter of its length from each end, part of the weight being retained by the raft above. All the remaining piles, which have been driven slightly lower, have false heads that include a nylon-sleeved cavity. When the tunnel section is in position on the four locating piles, cement grout is pumped under pressure into the nylon sleeves at the heads of the other piles, pushing their false heads up in contact with the tunnel section. As the pressure of the grout forced into each pile head is the same, the pressure of the tunnel section on every pile is equalized. All that remains is to allow the cement grout to set solid.

In constructing this new Rotterdam Metro the submerged-tube principle is being used to build the tunnel under the city streets as well as where it crosses the Maas River. A trench is first cut along the route of the tunnel (the tunnel has been sited along the line of wide streets where this was possible) and, since the water table is high, it is allowed to flood naturally with water. With the trenches full of water the heavy tunnel sections are floated into place (solving an otherwise difficult transport problem), and then sunk directly onto their prepared foundations prior to the joints being sealed. The trench is then refilled and the tunnel covered.

All long tunnels, but especially automobile tunnels, present a ventilation problem. The exhaust gases of the automobile include a small percentage of deadly carbon monoxide. If the percentage of this gas in the tunnel rises above a few parts in a thousand it can kill. Long tunnels therefore have ducts running longitudinally through them to carry fresh and stale air, these ducts being connected with the tunnel interior by suitably designed openings at regular intervals. The art of ensuring thorough ventilation with a minimum of power is a complex subject with which we cannot deal here. An idea of the size of the problem will be appreciated, however, in the following chapter where some details of the ventilation system in a typical tunnel are described.

7 Some Famous Tunnels

The Thames Tunnel

In the last chapter I mentioned Sir Marc Brunel's Thames tunnel, the world's first transportation tunnel under a navigable river, bored between 1824 and 1842 with the aid of Brunel's own invention, the tunneling shield. Perhaps the most remarkable aspect of this 353-m. twin tunnel was the fact that both carriageways were driven simultaneously, full size, from the start, without a pilot tunnel, without forced ventilation, every barrowful of clay and sand and mud being removed by hand from its huge, 7-m.-high, 19-m.-wide face. The brick lining, too, is notable. Built before the invention of Portland cement, it has remained entirely waterproof for a century and a quarter. Brunel used Roman cement (see page 20), had every individual brick hammer-tested before it was allowed into the shaft, and fired every bricklayer found to have laid a single loose brick. The side walls of the two finished vaulted archways were 1.5 m. thick, the floor and the arch crown each 1 m. Apart from continual seepage of stinking, sewage-laden

A portal of one of the two 2-km. tunnels built to provide navigation channels between trestle sections of the Chesapeake Bay bridge-tunnel, USA. These man-made islands at junction of trestle and tunnel are built of sand, stone, and concrete; the tunnels are double-skinned steel tubes, sunk in position.

Thames water through the working face, the men who built this tunnel had to face the inflow of pockets of methane gas (known in those days as "fire damp"), which burst into flame, ignited by the naked gas lamps used for illumination.

The tunnel was flooded several times by the river pouring through at the working face, and on each occasion the intrepid Marc Brunel saved a patently discouraging situation by sending down his son in a diving bell from a raft moored in the Thames above, to survey the position and extent of the breach in the river bed. This was then systematically plugged by dumping thousands of sacks of clay, pinning a huge tarpaulin over the mend, and then pumping dry the tunnel with steam pumps.

Brunel's shield was a remarkable affair. Consisting of 12 vertical cast-iron sections or frames, each pivoting on its foot, it protected the men behind it from the mud, clay, and sand ahead by a large number of stout horizontal oak timbers that they called *poling boards*. Each poling board could be removed independently from inside to enable a man to dig out the spoil directly ahead of it before forcing it forward into the void by means of its own small screw jacks acting as struts pushing against the frame. When the face in front of an entire frame had thus been excavated and all the poling boards advanced, the frame itself was then jacked bodily forward by simultaneously slackening off all the poling-board jacks and pushing with two huge master jacks fitted between the foot and head of the frame, and the invert and arch crown of the tunnel brickwork respectively. By thus moving one frame of the shield at a time into a space previously excavated section by section, very much less jacking force was required than is used with modern one-piece shields. As the height of the tunnel's working face, and therefore of each shield frame, was 7 m., it was divided into three cells, one above the other, each cell accommodating one laborer. The entire shield thus had 36 cells, and required 36 men at the face in each shift.

The Simplon Tunnel

Today, 60 years after its completion, the 20-km. Simplon tunnel under the Alps between Switzerland and Italy is still the deepest mainline railroad tunnel in the world. (The Japanese Tsugaru

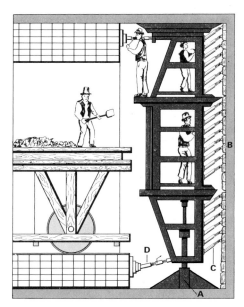

Side view of Sir Marc Brunel's shield for boring the Thames tunnel between 1824 and 1842. It consisted of 12 vertical cast-iron sections, each divided horizontally into three cells and pivoting on a foot (A). The men were protected by a number of wooden poling boards (B) provided with small screw jacks (C). When the entire face had been excavated, all the screw jacks were released and the shield moved forward by means of master jacks (D) between shield and brickwork at roof and floor.

tunnel—described briefly later in this chapter—will be longer, though much less deep. At one point the Simplon tunnel runs approximately 2100 m. below the crags of Monte Leone.) In many ways the Simplon represents the most difficult tunneling work ever undertaken; according to the historian Sulzer, had the dangers and obstacles faced and overcome been correctly anticipated, neither the engineers who built it nor any other "would have dared to undertake the contract."

The first great challenge faced the Italians who, after blasting their way 4.4 km. from the southern portal, hit soft decomposed rock (calcareous mica-schist) that was so "fluid" and under such pressure that even the heavy close timbering of the small pilot gallery was slowly but surely crushed. Work was stopped and the roof timbers were replaced with 40-cm. steel joists alternating with 50-cm. balks of pitch pine; but even this could not withstand the pressure. Finally rapid-hardening cement was forced into every gap; only then did the temporary lining hold.

The tunnel next had to be opened out to its full size and permanently lined. This was done step by step, every cut being shored up immediately with heavy timber; temporary brickwork was added between the pilot gallery and the inner line of the finished tunnel lining to give added strength while the 2-m.-thick masonry of this permanent lining was being laid.

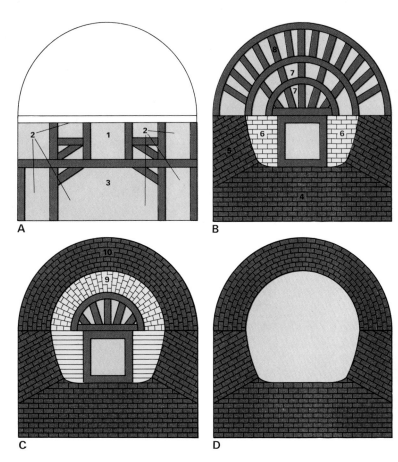

The second great obstacle was water. It was again the Italians who first ran into trouble, striking what they called "the Great Spring," from which water gushed at 48,000 liters per minute, the first outburst at a pressure of about 40 kg/cm². Fortunately for the Italians, they were working on a slight upgrade; the water flowed out naturally and only had to be sealed off. Due to the delays on the Italian side, the Swiss engineers, tunneling southward, completed their half of the tunnel much more rapidly. To save time it was agreed that they should push on beyond the halfway mark. It was then, nearly a kilometer further south, that the Swiss ran into a flood of hot water, and as their tunnel was on a downgrade they had the problem of pumping it out.

As a safety precaution against an uncontrolled inflow of hot water, iron safety doors were fitted, and when the Swiss later met

Opposite: stages in constructing the most difficult sections of the Simplon tunnel. (A) First, a pilot gallery (1) was bored, followed, as numbered, by the rest of the lower half of the tunnel, which was then supported by heavy temporary timberwork (brown). (B) Next, the lower half was supported with permanent masonry (red) and temporary brickwork (yellow) and the upper half dug out and supported with timberwork. (C) This timberwork was then replaced with first temporary, then permanent, brickwork and (D) all timberwork and temporary brickwork was removed.

an exceptionally hot spring releasing over 2250 l/min, work was abandoned and the doors sealed. It was now up to the Italians to push their way through and release the trapped hot water to flow out on the downgrade on their side of the tunnel. In the process the Italians first encountered more and hotter water. One spring produced 6300 l/min at a temperature of 47°c. The heat was so unbearable that a further 4500 l/min of cold water had to be pumped in and released as a spray at the working face in order to reduce the air temperature sufficiently for work to continue. When the Italians finally holed through to the Swiss heading, the hot water that was released in a torrent took half an hour to escape. The last 180 m. took the Italians six months to drive.

Today, though methods are not basically changed, tunnel blasting through hard rock is largely a routine. The most recent tunnel under the Alps, the 10-m.-wide 12-km. automobile tunnel under Mont Blanc, completed in 1965, presented no great engineering problems, although even on this project 17 men lost their lives, and one drilling jumbo was completely destroyed by a rock fall.

The Mersey Tunnel

The road tunnel under the River Mersey at Liverpool, England, though completed over 30 years ago, is still the largest-bore underwater road tunnel in the world. With an inside diameter of 15 m., the tunnel carries four traffic lanes (with space, never used, for two double-decker tramways below them), runs 3.2 km. from end to end, 1600 m. under the river, and descends to a maximum depth of 48 m. below water. The driving of this tunnel was conventional and gives a clear picture of the overall process.

Work began, of course, with a survey. This, and the records of the nearly parallel railroad tunnel built much earlier, disclosed

162

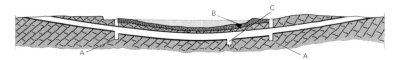

Above: longitudinal section of the Mersey road tunnel, showing the two service shafts (A), the glacial channel (B), and the drainage sump (C).

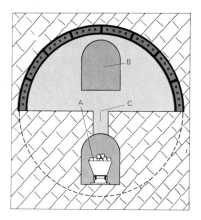

Left: intermediate stage in opening out the Mersey tunnel. First the lower pilot tunnel (A) was bored, followed by the upper pilot tunnel (B). Then the upper half was dug out, rock being dropped through a vertical shaft (C) into mine cars in the shaft below. The dotted line shows the line of the finished tunnel. Opposite: Mersey tunnel construction (north end) showing method of rock survey by test bores (black) and drain bores (blue). Also shown are the drain pilot tunnel (A), the lower pilot tunnel (B), the upper pilot tunnel (C). Broken lines show route of completed tunnel.

that the new road tunnel would have to be cut through sandstone, but that at one spot under the river, where there was a deep channel made by prehistoric glacial action, it might break out into loose rock overburden, or even into the silt of the river bed. The work had to be undertaken with this possibility in mind.

First, 7-m.-diameter vertical shafts were sunk near the river's banks, just off the line of the tunnel. Below the water table the sandstone was saturated and contained many water-bearing cracks and faults. To minimize the inflow of water, 5-cm. boreholes were driven into the sides of the shaft and cement mortar pumped into them under pressure. This cementation successfully controlled all flow from crevices and fissures. To control water seeping through the porous rock itself further pressure injections were made, this time of sodium silicate and aluminum sulfate, which successfully gelled to block the pores, cutting down water flow to one tenth, which could be handled easily by pumping.

The service shafts completed, a small working chamber was

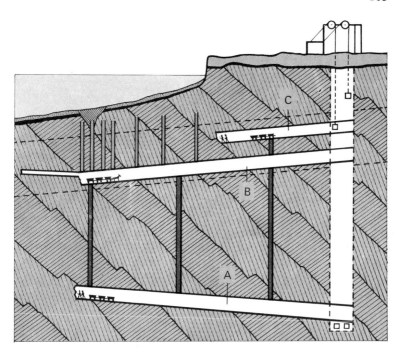

excavated to one side of each (the side where the tunnel was to pass) and from each of these, two 3-m.-diameter pilot tunnels were then driven, again by drilling and blasting, the lower always 45 m. ahead of the upper, each along the line of the tunnel. By keeping the lower pilot tunnel well ahead, the nature of the rock above it and the depth of the glacial channel that had to be passed could be checked by drilling boreholes upward from its roof. By this means the upper pilot tunnel, which in places was likely to be very near the upper limit of the rock, could be cut without the fear of a sudden breakthrough into the river mud, and the immense water pressure behind it.

In fact this prospecting by borehole resulted in a decision to lower the level of the main tunnel in order to avoid its breaking through into a gravel-filled crevice that was discovered below the glacial channel. Meanwhile, as the pilot tunnels continued, cementation and the injection of silicate was undertaken to control water flow and, at the Liverpool end (nearest to the glacial

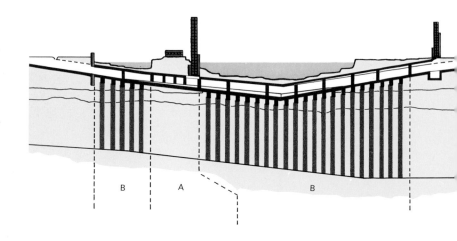

B   A   B

channel), a drain heading was also cut on an upward grade from the lowest point of the service shaft. Holes were drilled through from the pilot headings above to drain off all the uncontrolled water, which could then be pumped up from the bottom of the service shaft, which acted as a sump. Water seepage on the south side was so well controlled by the injection processes that a drain tunnel was considered unnecessary there.

Once the pilot tunnels from each end had met under the river, work was started on the job of opening out the main tunnel. The top half was completed first, the broken rock being dropped down through small vertical shafts into mine cars running on a track installed in the lower pilot tunnel, as shown in the diagram on page 162. Lining, made up of heavy cast-iron sections, was placed in position by a specially built segment erector, all joints being made watertight by packing with lead and bituminized hemp. The space remaining behind the lining segments was filled with broken rock, which was subsequently rendered solid by pumping in cement grout to fill all the remaining voids.

The upper half of the tunnel complete, the lower half was opened up and lined, the rock spoil now being removed by cars running overhead on a track suspended from the lining of the upper half of the tunnel.

The Mersey tunnel, being designed for automobile traffic, re-

Opposite: longitudinal section of the recently completed Ij road tunnel, Amsterdam. In addition to four caisson elements (A), nine prefabricated concrete sections (B) were sunk onto deep piles (red) that had been driven down through soft ground to reach solid bed anything up to 90 m. below ground level. Right: cross section of one of the prefabricated concrete sections showing automobile carriageways (A), service ducts (B), fresh and foul air ducts (C), and the PTFE bearings (D) between tunnel section and foundation bed (E) on its supporting piles.

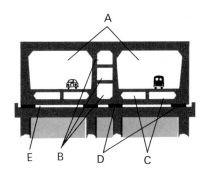

quired forced ventilation to ensure removal of the lethal carbon monoxide constituent of automobile exhaust gases. Designed to handle the exhaust effluent of four lanes of vehicles traveling at 25-m. intervals, the plant installed handles $2\frac{1}{4}$ million kg. of air each hour, distribution being by means of large ducts under the roadway and through slots leading up from the ducts throughout its length. Thirty huge fans (the largest 10 m. in diameter) operate constantly in six buildings, some pumping fresh air into the under-road ducts, others sucking foul air out from above. This tunnel was opened to traffic in 1934, cost $18 million at the time, and was financed by the collection of tolls.

The Ij Road Tunnel

A more recent four-lane road tunnel at present being built under the Ij estuary in Amsterdam, Holland (and due for completion in 1968), will be half the length of the Mersey tunnel, but provides a useful demonstration of the technique of sinking prefabricated units.

The huge tunnel elements vary from 70 to 90 m. in length, and weigh up to 17 million kg. each. They contain twin 7-m. roadways, side by side, with a central service channel and under-road ducts for fresh and foul air. Made of reinforced concrete, they are rendered watertight by means of a 0.75-cm. steel skin on the bottom and sides and a bituminous membrane along the top. Fabricated in a nearby dry dock built especially for the purpose, and floated to the site with temporary concrete bulkheads, they are sunk onto a prepared foundation in a submarine trench prepared by dredging. The foundation is a concrete slab supported along its length by 113-cm.-diameter piles driven down through the very soft ground to a solid bed, found between 65 and 80 m. below ground level. Between the foundation and the tunnel elements are PTFE bearings that allow the elements to slide if necessary—they are joined together with bellows-type expansion joints that allow for movement caused by temperature changes or minor subsidence of the piles. To allow for immediate post-assembly settlement (which might be as much as 4 cm.) each section is built with two hinges, each with watertight double-skinned steel bellows, the longitudinal steel reinforcement passing unbroken through these joints, which will be made rigid, when settlement is complete, by filling the gap inside the bellows with concrete.

Four shorter sections of this tunnel, which are to carry above them a ventilation building and a railroad embankment, will be constructed differently—concreted on site within sheet piling, using compressed air to exclude the water.

The Chesapeake Bay Tunnels

One of the boldest prefabricated underwater tunnel projects forms part of the remarkable 28-km. Chesapeake Bay bridge-tunnel, USA, completed in 1964 and illustrated on page 156. Basically a low-level precast prestressed-concrete trestle construction (20 km. are spanned by these trestles), the project was required to provide four wide high-level navigation channels. Two of the channels were spanned by bridges, but the other two were provided by sinking tunnels, each about 2 km. long, way out in mid-bay, the transitions from trestle to tunnel and back being achieved by the construction of four man-made islands, built of sand, stone, and concrete, each 450 m. long, and 70 m. wide.

The tunnel sections of this project were double-skinned steel tubes, 90 m. long, towed from the Texas Gulf coast as empty buoyant shells, then sunk into position in a dredged trench by filling their hollow walls with concrete.

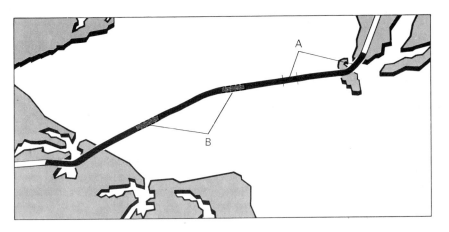

The Chesapeake Bay bridge-tunnel between Virginia (left) and Maryland (right), USA. The scheme provides four navigation channels, two spanned by bridges (A) and two by sunken prefabricated tunnel sections (B); the rest of the link consists of the trestle causeway seen in the photograph on page 156.

Another notable bridge-tunnel complex that deserves mention carries the six-lane Trans-Canada highway across the St. Lawrence Seaway. The underwater section of this Louis Hippolyte Lafontaine crossing, totaling 756 m., is built of seven 36-m.-wide, 8-m.-high, and 108-m.-long prefabricated immersed concrete sections. There is, too, the 9.6-km. railroad tunnel project that will soon carry the San Francisco rapid-transit railroad across the bay, 40 m. below water level, 6.4 km. being of immersed tube, concrete in a steel skin, accommodating two 5-m. railroad tracks and ventilation ducts.

The Seikan Undersea Railroad Tunnel

Japanese engineers are currently at work on what will be the world's longest underwater tunnel, a 36-km. tube bored through rock under the 22-km. Tsugaru strait dividing Japan's main island (Honshu) from the northern island of Hokkaido.

The channel is deep, plunging to 140 m. below sea level. Though many years of geological survey have preceded the start of actual tunneling, the nature of the partly volcanic submarine rock appears so unpredictable that the engineers decided a pilot tunnel should be bored before work on the main tunnel is started. And since the main tunnel will necessarily slope downward under the sea—a potentially dangerous situation where unforeseen water-bearing rock faults might result in rapid high-pressure flooding—the 3-m.-

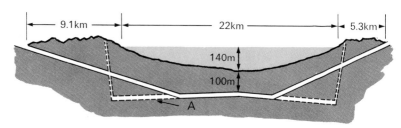

168

Longitudinal section of the proposed 36-km. Seikan tunnel linking Japan's main island (Honshu) with the northern island of Hokkaido. The unpredictable nature of the submarine rock and the danger of flooding made it necessary to start with a 3-m.-diameter pilot tunnel (A), which will eventually become a permanent drainage tunnel. For added safety the bore is being kept a clear 100 m. below the deepest point in the strait.

diameter pilot tunnel is being driven on an upward grade from deep shafts on each shore. It will serve, ultimately, as a permanent drainage tunnel. For added safety the line of the bore is being kept a clear 100 m. below the deepest point in the strait; this means that the pilot tunnel will run (as will the main tunnel) some 240 m. below sea level. Only when the pilot bore is complete (target date is the end of 1969) will the engineers decide whether a single 10-m.-diameter tunnel or twin tubes of 6.2 m. diameter will be the more practicable. Either way the plan is to work on the main tunnel from 10 separate headings, all accessible from the pilot bore and its access shafts. The Japanese are investigating three problems while the pilot tunnel is being completed: They will test the effectiveness of various injection processes against high-pressure leakage in rock, and select the most effective for use during boring of the main tunnel, test existing hard-rock tunneling machines and develop a machine best suited for the project, and develop improved rock-blasting procedures. Completion of the Seikan tunnel is provisionally planned for 1975.

A Tunnel Collapses

The construction engineer working on a tunnel project is sometimes faced with an unforeseen problem far greater than flooding or the inflow of subterranean gas. What he does when rock pressure is so great and its constitution so brittle that the roof of the bore literally collapses, is necessarily dependent on the circumstances. He must make immediate decisions and act fast.

Britain's east-west mainline railroad between Sheffield and Manchester traverses the Pennine mountain ridge through a 4.8-km. double-line tunnel, completed in 1953 to replace two much older single-line bores. The newer 10-m.-diameter tunnel was opened up from a 4-m.-square pilot heading. The engineers who built this tunnel found the stable sandstone interrupted, between 210 and 240 m. from the west portal, by a 24-m. sloping stratum of water-bearing shale. As a precaution against trouble, structural steel ribs were put into the main tunnel at 4-m. intervals from about 30 m. ahead of the point where the fault was first met in the pilot heading. Despite these immensely strong ribs, which had considerable longitudinal packing behind them, the steelwork began to show signs of strain after a few days' installation. Additional packing appeared to halt the movement, but some four days later the steel in the crown of the tunnel again began to distort.

The addition of more ribs was considered too dangerous and all men and equipment were immediately withdrawn from the working face and the area where the pilot heading was being enlarged. A few hours later the roof of the tunnel collapsed over a length of 22 m., bringing tons of broken rock and twisted steel down into the tunnel and leaving a huge rounded cavity above.

Longitudinal and cross sections showing extent of the rock fall in the Woodhead tunnel disaster, England, in 1951. Diagram shows (left) the limits of first (A) and second (B) falls, and (right) the cavity formed above the tunnel section in relation to the tunnel ribs.

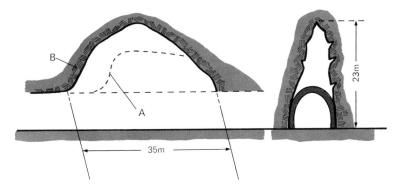

Method used to limit roof fall during construction of the Woodhead railroad tunnel, England. After collapse of 30 m. of tunnel, the massive concrete bulkhead seen here was built across the tunnel, and debris cautiously excavated through the central recess opening. An especially thick section of lining was then built and the concrete bulkhead removed.

The engineer in charge immediately undertook strengthening of the tunnel directly west of the collapse by the addition of more steel ribs, but a fortnight later a further section of the roof gave way, increasing the collapsed length to about 30 m. To prevent further complications a massive concrete bulkhead was now built right across the tunnel, as close as possible to the collapsed section, to support the weakened crown, a suitable hole being left for access through the bulkhead.

The problem now was to clear the debris beyond the bulkhead, prevent further collapse, and continue the construction of the tunnel. At first it was decided to try filling the void above the fallen material with concrete pumped down through boreholes made from the ground surface above. When survey showed how enormous the cavity was, the plan was changed; instead men began to clear the debris by working through the hole in the bulkhead, under the protection of a steel hood supported by girders made up of military bridging units cantilevered forward as they advanced. As the tunnel area was cleared, steel ribs conforming to the planned shape of the finished tunnel were immediately erected at 30-cm. intervals; longitudinal formwork was then fitted and concrete piped behind until a 1-m.-thick arch had been formed, the cavity above remaining empty. Though slow, this method proved successful, and when the entire collapsed section had been cleared and lined with a 1-m. mass-concrete arch over steel ribs, this arch was lined by thickening to 1.5 m., leaving the steel ribs inside the added concrete as reinforcement. This unusual repair work over 30 m. of tunnel took just six months, compared with the three weeks taken to open out the original bore.

The English Channel Tunnel

The tunnel with the longest history, but which has yet to be built, is the proposed tunnel linking England and France under the Straits of Dover. First promoted in 1802, this most elusive of all tunnel projects has passed through many phases. Historians record 20 major schemes, of which 5 were for single tubes, 6 (including the currently approved plan) for twin single-line railroad tunnels, and 9 (including, surprisingly, the first and the most recent) for the newest of tunnel types, the immersed prefabricated tube. There have also been several schemes for bridges.

A Frenchman, Thomé de Gamond, devoted his entire life to the tunnel. He promoted several realistic schemes, including the first to be officially approved by the British and French governments, a stone-lined, twin-track railroad tunnel proposed in 1856. De Gamond was also joint sponsor in 1867, with an English engineer, William Low, of a twin-tube railroad tunnel that, in many respects, is similar to the tunnel likely to be constructed today.

The current scheme (prepared between 1958 and 1960), unlike all those promoted earlier, is soundly based on exhaustive geological studies. Techniques used included geophysical prospecting by two audiofrequency systems. These, by measuring the time lapse between sound waves reflected from the successive boundaries of the various underwater strata, provided the data for a reasonably accurate geological section of the seabed down to a depth of 50 m. and more. Physical examination of the seabed was conducted by frogmen, who obtained nearly 400 samples (taken from 40–50 cm. below the bed level) for laboratory examination—including microscopic indentification of fossils. Deep borings were made along the proposed line of the tunnel, four on shore (the deepest, near the French coast, penetrating 270 m.) and eight under the sea (where the deepest was pushed 70 m. into the seabed under 40 m. of water). In addition, the 2-m. pilot heading bored at Sangatte, near Calais, in 1882 by the Beaumont machine (see page 000) was pumped out and examined. Experts found its bare chalk walls in excellent condition, and little seepage.

The somewhat astonishing result of this recent technical survey was to confirm the assumptions made by engineer de Gamond a century ago—assumptions based largely on inspired guesswork. The Frenchman had selected the best possible route for his tunnel —probably the only one where he might have succeeded in those days of relatively primitive engineering technology. The survey demonstrated the existence, under the Straits of Dover, of a continuous formation of impervious chalk varying from 70 m. thick near the French coast to 85 m. under the cliffs of Dover. Though some faults were found parallel to the proposed line of the tunnel, none were detected running across it. The survey was followed by engineering studies that considered four basic alternatives: a tunnel bored by machine through the lower chalk, an immersed tube laid in a dredged channel on the seabed, a bridge, and a bridge-tunnel.

All four plans were technically feasible. Machines existed that could cut a tunnel through the chalk to its full diameter, and the slurry method of pumping out spoil was suited to the material. The development (in undersea oil and gas prospecting) of huge floating platforms with retractable stabilizer legs made the immersed-tube technique feasible even in up to 85 m. of choppy seawater. Engineers considered the building of a continuous bridge within the bounds of existing experience. A bridge-tunnel was also possible because of the existence of the Colbert and Varne banks, where the sea is relatively shallow (only a few meters at low water), these being conveniently situated about one third and two thirds of the way along the proposed route. The bridge and bridge-tunnel schemes were quickly eliminated on financial grounds. Although the traffic capacity of a continuous rail-cum-road bridge would have been considerably greater than that of a tunnel, traffic forecasts indicated that the potential earning capacity could never justify the high capital cost (about $540 million at 1960 prices). A bridge-tunnel would have cost even more.

Therefore the choice lay between a bored and an immersed tube tunnel; and in each case there was the alternative of a railroad and an automobile crossing. The latter required a fully ventilated tube of at least 12 m. diameter—the former, self-ventilating twin 7-m. tubes. An immersed-tube automobile tunnel (at a cost of $312 million) was found to be the least expensive, but with only one lane in each direction its traffic (and therefore earning) capacity was severely limited. Next cheapest proved to be the twin-bore railroad tunnel, which, including rail installations and terminals, was estimated to cost $330 million and to earn a considerably higher revenue.

So it is to be a 51-km. twin 7-m. railroad tunnel, 37 km. running under the sea. There will be cross passages and four crossover junctions, also a central 3.3-m. service tunnel that will be driven ahead of the main tubes as a pilot bore. Longitudinally the tunnel will form a shallow W with a central high point about 40 m. below the seabed, which at that point will be nearly 50 m. below sea level. Two drainage galleries will drain water from the low point of the W to deep pumping shafts at the French and English coasts. The main tubes will be lined with 45-cm.-thick concrete.

Traction will be electric, of course, with current at 25,000 V. Trains will depart every 5 to 10 minutes at peak hours, with direct London-Paris and London-Brussels services. Also there are to be frequent flat-wagon two-deck automobile trains with especially designed no-delay drive-on terminals, this service alone having a planned capacity of over 6000 vehicles an hour. If Thomé de Gamond conceived his tunnel on faith and imagination, the current scheme is based on proven technology. Today's planners mean business.

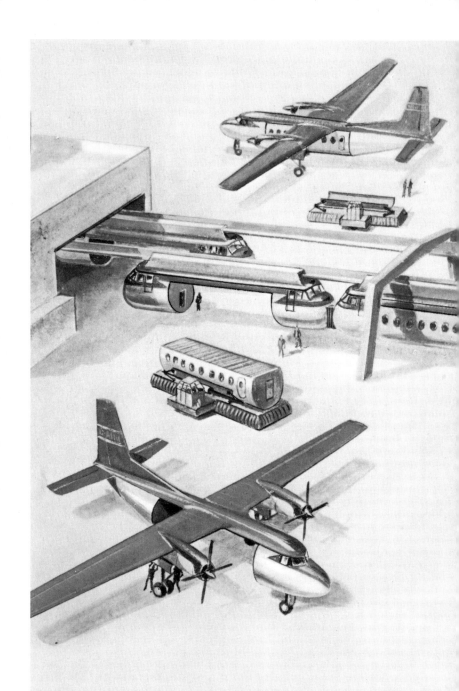

8 The Future

Roads

In Chapter 2 I mentioned the 1963 World Roads Congress estimate of the world's automobile population—150 million vehicles, enough to stretch over 20 times around the world, nose to tail; also the estimated 35.2 million km. of highways, which allows a comfortable 225 m. of road for each vehicle, This sounds fine. Yet wherever our planet's population has agglomerated into great conurbations, we see a very different picture emerging. "Unless London gets a new road pattern its suburbs will have seized up in 15 years' time," screamed a London newspaper in July 1966, when the results of a major traffic survey were announced. The warning concerned an area of 2600 km²—for that is the size of greater London.

Already we know the world's likely road patterns in 1975. The US program of construction aims to achieve a total of 65,600 km. of freeways. At an only slightly less impressive pace Europe is completing 41,600 km. of international through routes agreed at

A terminal in a pod or module scheme for bridging the gap between land and air transport. While modules are moved to waiting aircraft, empty trains are moved to the outgoing mono-rail to receive incoming modules. The scheme integrates air and land transport in a unified transport system.

an all-Europe convention. Great new highways are being built across Russia, China, and South America. Even a small country such as Japan is well advanced in a program designed to complete 4000 km. of freeways. Only Africa, of the major continents, seems to be behind the times in terms of highway length per unit of its sprawling area. But for all the impressive road-building programs the problem of human transportation is escalating beyond the capacity of the conventional highway to solve. Add to the world's great road programs the expanding rapid-transport railroad systems and multiplying air services, and still, for every step forward, 20th-century urban society finds itself a step behind in the race. This is a problem that requires, and is now getting, decisive rethinking. But every bright thought today begets a new engineering problem tomorrow. What will tomorrow's civil engineers be doing? That is what interests us.

Of course there will be new freeways, rural and urban, the latter with elevated roadways piercing and encircling the hearts of cities. Of course there will be new interurban rapid transit railroads. Of course there will be new airfields and rooftop heliports for intercity air traffic. All these will be built by tomorrow's engineers; but they will design in a new idiom, and build a new concept of transportation engineering, that we can only hint at today. The urban freeways will rise up over city suburbs, plunge into the heart of city centers, and break up into distribution deltas of locality feeder routes, serving every area without merging with the pedestrian arcades above and below, linked everywhere with multistorey or underground parking. The new high-speed intercity freeways may be automated, radar beams monitoring the path of each automobile, taking over the controls and driving it at upward of 150 km/h by automatic electronic pilot while the driver relaxes, shaves perhaps, enjoys coffee and rolls, or makes radiotelephone calls until the automatic pilot warns him to take over the controls as the automobile slows and enters the feeder system of his city destination. The rapid transit railroads may glide

The present US program of road construction aims to achieve a total of nearly 66,000 km. of freeway by 1975. The map shows the 1966 freeway system (red) together with those planned for completion by 1975 (blue).

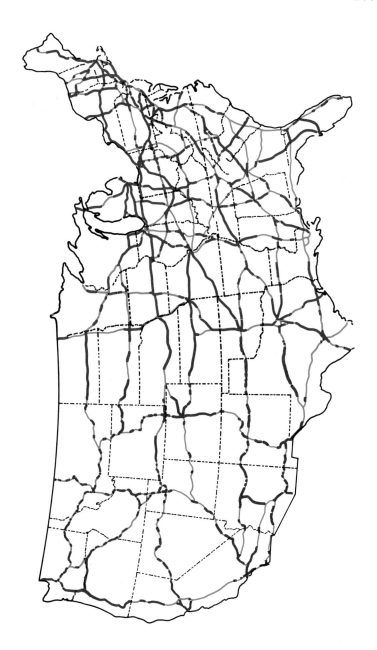

on elevated monorails, borne on air bearings, at speeds of 300 km/h or more, their frequency and speed controlled by computer so that there is a seat for every ticket holder, and none wasted. Or these trains may plunge into the earth in evacuated tubes. There may be long-distance intercity automobile railroads: the traveler drives into a large glass-sided wagon, parks, and strolls along to the restaurant-bar-saloon, to have a meal, relax, play a hand of poker perhaps, while the train speeds him and his car a thousand dust-free kilometers in two or three comfortable hours. The airports may be perched on the top of city-center office blocks, from which 100-seater vertical-takeoff air-buses propel travelers off to their destination without the wasted time and effort of taking a bus down to the old airport pickup center, a limousine to the busy airfield, and even then a 20-minute wait while the flight gets takeoff clearance. And, of course, all these visions of man's future answers to his transportation problems mean new and more and greater projects for the civil engineer.

Bridges

Let us take a more detailed forward glance at the future, and see what else the civil engineer of A.D. 2000 will be building for his living in the field of transportation. As American writer Jo Gies has put it: "A bridge is to a road what a diamond is to a ring." There have been, and are, bridges that can claim space in the history books of architecture (even, in the creative hands of Maillart, Freyssinet, and others, a foothold, if an uneasy one, in the province of modern art). But the chief appeal of the bridge throughout the ages has been the appeal of wonder—of fascination, and of admiration for the men who conceived and built them.

Before we can look intelligently into the future of bridge building, before we can make a realistic prophecy, we must examine today's theoretical limits.

Clearly there is no limit, at least in theory, to empirical strength. If a steel arch can carry a live load of 250,000 kg., then four such arches placed side by side should be able to carry over 1 million kg. If a suspension bridge has a given strength with two main cables, it should have double the strength with four cables suspended from twin towers. Unfortunately this concept collapses—

like the overlong bridge—in terms of span. If a 150-m. bridge weighs 9,500,000 kg., and carries a live load of 500,000 kg., its total weight-carrying capacity, live and dead, is clearly 10 million kg. Doubling this bridge's span will double its weight, and turn the scales at 19 million kg. if the girder section remains the same. At once we see that the bridge's own dead weight has far exceeded its total carrying capacity. The bridge will carry no live load, and simply break its back. This calculation, needless to say, is a monstrous simplification, but the inference is correct.

This principle, rightly applied, means that for each bridge material, and for each design, there is a theoretical limit to the span at which the bridge's weight overtakes its strength. (There is an exception to this, as we shall see, but it is to all intents and purposes true in practice.)

The longest extant steel cantilever span today is the 540-m. Quebec bridge. The theoretical limit, using the strongest contemporary structural steel, is not much more than 750 m. Theodore Cooper did well when he designed his Quebec bridge half a century ago, to say nothing of Sir Benjamin Baker's achievement with his two 513-m. Forth railroad bridge spans, erected 30 years earlier still.

The steel arch builders do not seem to have done quite so well. The record stands with the 496-m. span shared, give or take a few centimeters, by the Bayonne (New York) and Sydney Harbor bridges, both completed a little over 30 years ago. But the theoretical limit for a steel arch, based on the strength/weight ratio of today's strongest structural steel works out at almost double—some 1000 m.

We have seen that reinforced concrete, especially in its prestressed form, is making rapid headway in the field of bridging; and it is reasonable to predict that this material will make continuing inroads into the former preserves of steel, bridging wider and wider gaps. The longest concrete arch today, the Gladesville bridge at Sydney, leaps over 305 m. of water, and was built with the aid of falsework. Yet the late Eugène Freyssinet, with all the weight of his massive reputation, proposed a 1000-m. concrete arch as long ago as 1930, and later stated that his 150-m. Caracas-La Guaira mountain freeway bridges could be taken as models for the erection, without ground-supported falsework, of such huge concrete arches. He should know.

Suspension bridges already span 1280 m. in one great leap. Already there are plans for a 1375-m. suspension span across the mouth of Britain's River Humber. Another of almost equal length has been proposed to cross Britain's River Mersey between Liverpool and Birkenhead. And a bridge of 1470 m. span is on the drawing board to cross Japan's inland sea. Yet another suspension bridge, of 1500 m. span, has been designed to cross the strait between Italy and Sicily, and there is talk of still one more, of similar length, to bridge the Bosphorus. But even these are nowhere near the theoretical limit for bridges of this type using contemporary design principles and contemporary materials; experienced designers have suggested a span of over 3000 m. as technically feasible. These figures, if impressive, assume today's materials, today's designs—not tomorrow's. Surely we should be naïve in this age of technological upset to presume no new breakthrough in either field. In the design field a new concept in prestressed concrete has already been incorporated in the design of a bridge to cross Lake Geneva. Let us look at this proposal in rather more detail.

I stated, on page 179, that there is an exception to the proposition that for every material of which a bridge can be made there is a span limit when weight overtakes strength. I also mentioned much earlier, on page 26, that, at least in theory, a prestressed-concrete beam can be designed to carry its own weight. These two statements are, in fact, different facets of the same truth. And it is the theory of the stressed ribbon bridge that attempts to make a practical prestressed-concrete structure that will almost carry its own weight. But the revolutionary idea here is that the concrete is used primarily *in tension*, by prestressing so that this tension is never felt by the concrete, spending itself entirely in overcoming the prestress. The design for the Lake Geneva bridge relies on a continuous 25-cm.-thick slab of concrete reinforced with four layers of prestressed 2.5-cm.-diameter high-tensile steel bars, the steel to occupy no less than 25 per cent of the total concrete cross section. The slab, which is itself to be the road deck, is to be suspended in an almost imperceptible funicular curve—so shallow that its mean radius would be 3000 m. The design incorporates 100-m. projecting cantilevers, from the ends of which 240-m. ribbons will be suspended, making total spans of 450 m.

To cross Lake Geneva, Ulrich Finsterwalder, the German designer, envisages three of these 450-m. spans alternating with two of 200 m. each, the latter being represented by the two balancing arms of adjoining cantilevers. During construction it is intended that the steel bars, suspended first, will carry the formwork for the concrete ribbon, this to be cast in situ with provision, presumably, for post-tensioning the steel. This is not a great span; but the idea is something quite new, something that might well be developed. True, the principle of suspending the steel bars first to support the formwork for the concrete ribbon itself limits the span. But other construction methods may subsequently be adopted so that the superior strength/weight ratio of the finished prestressed ribbon can be exploited from the start.

While this is partly sound engineering design, it is as yet untested and so partly conjecture. But if at first glance the whole idea appears frighteningly insecure, remember that so did the now conventional suspension span before Roebling built his first fantastic 250-m. double-deck railroad-cum-automobile bridge across the gaping Niagara Falls ravine in 1855. Bridges four times as long were built on Roebling's principle within 50 years of the Niagara bridge's opening.

As for the field of new materials, developments may prove as astonishing as they are unpredictable. Already Nylon 66 is made with a tensile strength about one sixth that of high-tensile steel wire; yet it is incomparably lighter, and completely proof against atmospheric corrosion. No doubt it is very much more elastic; but this can surely be allowed for in design. It is weakened by moisture; can it not have a waterproof coating? Reinforce it with glass fiber and perhaps we shall find we have a potential suspension bridge cable material with twice the span potential of today's strongest steel wire. Aluminum, too, is being made immensely strong by the incorporation of glass "whisker" reinforcement. This is only in the early experimental stage, but these experiments may well bear fruit.

What about concrete materials? Might it not be possible to substitute stone aggregate with chunks of some plastic developed especially for its crushing strength, making concrete of today's strength but, perhaps, half or even less than half the weight? By applying the prestressing techniques to our new lightweight concrete, using our glass fiber-reinforced nylon in place of steel wire, we might then have a material so strong for its weight that we could bridge the 14.4-km. Straits of Gibraltar, and so fulfil a contemporary version of one of the Victorian engineer's most exciting dreams—a railroad (in today's motor age it would, of course, be an autmobile freeway) from London, via the Channel Tunnel and the Gibraltar bridge, to Cape Town.

Tunnels

What of the future of tunnels? The Japanese are confident that a 36.8-km. under-sea railroad tunnel is practicable. The Americans are developing machines that bite their way through solid rock as automatically as the well-established clay-tunneling machines. Where the new tunnels will be is anyone's guess. The Channel Tunnel will surely, at last, be built. Today there is no technical problem. The capital can be raised without government participation. The two governments seem now to have no political or military objections.

The most advanced tunnel proposal published in recent years is the long-distance evacuated tube—an American's ingenious plan to help solve the United States' snowballing east-coast transport problem. The designer decided to break uncompromisingly with tradition. With his associates he formulated three basic assumptions:

1. To compete with air travel the system must provide an average speed along the Boston-Washington route of 320 km/h. Allowing for stops this implies a cruising speed in the region of 640 km/h.
2. To protect any moving vehicles at such high speeds from ice, birds, or other objects in its path, it must be accommodated in a continuous tube.
3. To eliminate air resistance, which would preclude such rapid passage through a tube, the latter must be evacuated.

Developing these assumptions into a workable proposition

Artist's impression of the rigs proposed for laying the English Channel tunnel by the immersed tube method. The rigs (one for digging the shallow trench, one for laying the tube sections) have retractable legs: When a section is complete, a sliding section of the deck moves forward and legs are lowered; the legs of the rear section are then raised and it too slides forward. In this way the rigs "walk" their way across, laying the tunnel as they go.

resulted in four design decisions briefly described below:

1. Since the tubes would be evacuated, the most economical method of propelling the trains through them would be by admitting air at atmospheric pressure behind them. Since the trains would be moving into a vacuum, the atmospheric friction that absorbs almost all the enormous power required to propel vehicles through the air at high speeds would be absent. Consequently four 1875-KW. electric motors driving air pumps at one or two points outside the tube would be sufficient to achieve the planned transit speeds. (For a conventional through-air vehicle, atmospheric drag at the planned speeds at sea level approximates 52,500 KW.) Acceleration up to and over 480 km/h would be achieved without expenditure of power by means of downgrades leading out of each station to a suggested standard tunnel level 1000 m. underground, the corresponding upgrade as a train approached each station acting as a frictionless brake.

2. There should be a pair of tubes, for two-way traffic, side by side.

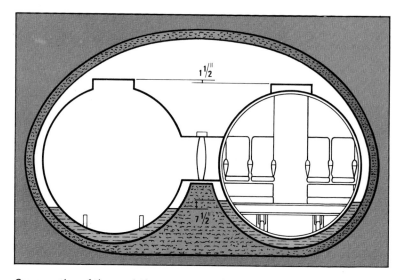

Cross section of the revolutionary evacuated tunnel rapid transport system proposed to link Boston and Washington, USA. The trains fit snugly into the tubes like pistons in a cylinder, and the tubes themselves float on water to ensure perfect suspension, providing a cruising speed of around 640 km/h. An underground system was found to be cheaper than a surface link, with its high cost in real estate, bridging, and tunneling.

3. In view of the enormous cost of real estate acquisition, bridging, and tunneling for a reasonably straight and level surface siting of the tubes, it was decided to place the entire 640-km. system in a deep tunnel. A realistic costing, using modern rock-tunneling machinery, suggested that such a tunnel would cost less, rather than more, than a conventional high-speed surface railroad, such as the 240 km/h Tokaido line linking Tokyo with Osaka.

4. An underground tunnel could be perfectly level, making it possible to float each transit tube on water in a channel of only slightly larger bore; this would provide highly efficient hydraulic cushioning.

To give an idea of how efficient this system could be, the designers concluded it would be no problem to operate up to six trains an hour in each direction. As each train would accommodate up to 1600 seated passengers and an equal number standing during the rush hour if necessary, the system would have a rush-hour top capacity of 18,000 passengers an hour in each direction. This is considerably more than the predicted demand for many years to come despite the present acute shortage of facilities. A train leaving Boston at 13.15 hours would reach Providence at 13.23 and move on after 2 minutes. With five other 2-minute stops en route and a 5-minute halt at New York the train would finally reach Washington at 14.45, exactly 90 minutes out of Boston, after a run exceeding 640 km.

Does all this sound like a schoolboy's dream? In fact it is a serious proposal that originated as a study at the Space Systems Division of the Lockheed Missiles and Space Company, California, USA, has received detailed theoretical examination, and

The Aerotrain, France's monorail hovertrain, reaching speeds of over 300 km/h on a test run near Paris. Powered by a piston aero-engine driving a three-blade propeller and with air-cushion suspension operating at high speeds, this looks like being a useful contribution to world problems of rapid commuter transportation.

is considered not only technically but also financially feasible. Civil engineers may well have to cut those 640-km. tubes through the bedrock.

Finally, what of the future of the railroad? Full electrification of main lines will push ahead as rapidly as capital formation allows. All-electric traction has many advantages. But it is in the rapid transit field that we shall see the railroad hitting the world's headlines. The San Francisco computer-controlled, rubber-tired commuter system will be completed, proved, emulated, and greatly improved. The monorail principle, exemplified in the Japanese line linking Tokyo city center with its international airport, and providing a 15-minute service running at 6-minute intervals during rush hours over the 12.8-km. route, will also find favor. And the remarkable linear electric motor propelling a train without moving parts, suspended in a magnetic field, that is currently under development in Britain will perhaps become as commonplace as the clattering underground city railways of today.

By A.D. 2000 the world of transport will be hardly recognizable to the average traveler of 1967. Roads, bridges, tunnels, railroads, airports—all these will be incomparably finer in concept, design, and achievement than they are today. It will be the concept, the design, and the achievement of the civil engineer.

Suggested Reading

Roads

A. Legault, *Highway and Airport Engineering,* Prentice-Hall
(Englewood Cliffs, New Jersey and London, 1960)
C. H. Oglesby and L. I. Hewes, *Highway Engineering*, 2nd Edition,
John Wiley, (New York and London, 1963)
R. C. and S. K. Sharma, *Principles and Practice of Civil Engineering,*
Taplinger Publishing Company (New York, 1964)
Asia Publishing (London, 1965)

Bridges

J. Gies, *Bridges and Men,* Doubleday (Garden City, New York, 1963)
Cassell (London, 1964)
D. Y. Hill, *Bridge Calculation and Design,* 2nd Edition,
Griffin (London, 1962)
R. E. Rowe, *Concrete Bridge Design and Supplement,* Contractor's Record
(London, 1962) John Wiley (New York, 1963)
H. Shirley-Smith, *The World's Greatest Bridges,* 2nd Edition,
Phoenix House (London, 1964) Harper and Row (New York, 1965)
I. M. Viest, R. S. Fountain, and R. C. Singleton, *Composite Construction
in Steel and Concrete*, McGraw-Hill (New York, 1958; London, 1959)

Tunnels

G. Gries, *Adventure Underground,* Doubleday (Garden City, New York, 1959)
Hale (London, 1962)
R. Hammond, *Tunnel Engineering,* Macmillan (New York, 1959) Heywood
(London, 1959)
C. A. Pequignot (Ed.) *Tunnels and Tunneling,* Macmillan (New York, 1963)
Hutchinson (London, 1963)
G. E. Sandstrom, *Tunnels,* Holt, Rinehart, and Winston (New York, 1963)
Barrie & Rockliff (London, 1963)

Index

Page numbers in *italics* refer to illustrations.